A
MATTER
OF
CHOOSING

Eda Lord

Simon and Schuster   New York   1963

This book is a novel. The characters (with the exception of Dean Yost of Stanford and a reference to former President Herbert Hoover) are all fictitious and are not intended to bear resemblance to any living persons.

BL

MAY   3 '63

to Tania Stern

My lines and life are free; free as the road,
Loose as the winds, as large as store.

—GEORGE HERBERT

This novel probes the difficulties of a young girl forced to make adult decisions before possessing sufficient knowledge and experience.

I

"It is for you to make the choice."

Neither of us moved, as though a lens had clicked open for a time exposure. My grandmother was a voice, an indistinct figure on the chaise longue. Propped against it, her slender ebony stick reflected a point of light which came through the open French windows of the drawing room. Here in the patio the air was soft and dark and scented with jasmine. It was my first night in Southern California, my first encounter with my grandmother for many years, I was entering a world lapped by ease and gentleness of nature.

I embraced this world; I wanted everything to be as different from my life in Wisconsin as it possibly could be.

I said my choice was the private school. What I did not

7

say was that the prospect of being spoiled and pampered, which my grandmother had described as a possible danger, had only aroused longing. She had left an open path; dispassionately, she had pointed out the advantages and disadvantages: the higher scholastic standard of the private school, the expense, perhaps false values. In contrast, high school was more democratic and gave greater freedom, but reports of the students' behavior after school hours were disturbing. *Necking,* a terrible word. She spoke it distantly as though held at arm's length in fire tongs.

My grandmother was saying how impossible it was to decide for other people. When she had sent me to my aunt in Wisconsin after my father died, she had thought it the best solution—cousins to play with, animals; all children loved farms, she had thought. Apparently she had been wrong.

"I am too old to adjust my ways to youth." Oddly enough, this phrase made me feel I had come home; it was the formula she had always welcomed me with in the past. She went on to say that this, the last house she would ever build, was small—one must march with the times—servants were hard to find and hard to keep.

I was facing the garden: a triptych of blackness framed by cool arches and delicate twisted columns. The stars hung close. "You have made it very beautiful," I said.

I would find that she lived informally; often she dined out with friends or at the hotel. This would not do for me if I were going to school. She felt no inclination to alter her life. I would have to manage somehow on my own. I was almost a woman now, sixteen, wasn't I? If I could do that—

8

find my own way and be happy—she was quite prepared to have me live with her.

I could not think what else to say: I said she was very kind.

After a while the beauty of the night hushed us into silence. At last, my grandmother said she was going in to bed. Since her accident (a taxi had knocked her down and this had broken her hip) she found she tired easily. It had happened only four months ago and she supposed she ought to be grateful that the bone had mended. The doctor said it was remarkable in anyone over seventy. The leg would always be slightly shorter than the other. She hated the limp and depending on a stick—she was used to moving swiftly—she hated growing old. It should be constantly in my mind that I possessed the greatest treasure of all—youth. Every day I ought to wake up happy that I was young. She did not suppose that I did so, and she was quite right.

She found it the most outrageous inadequacy of life that experience could not be passed on to others. Each human being had to find out for himself. So stupid. Such waste.

She stood up while she was talking, as though to prevent any gesture of help. For a moment she leaned on her stick, so that when she started to walk, she moved without hesitation. I shut and locked the French windows and turned out the lights in the drawing room. The moon was rising over the mountain and filled the room and lit the corridor with its light. My grandmother waited at my door facing the open windows, the moon and Soledad, that black mountain bare as an elephant's back. It was to become as familiar as the room; indeed, it was part of it. She said she hoped I would be happy here, offered her cheek and was gone.

I shut the door and was instantly aware of the sense of liberation that comes from the shutting of the door to a room of one's own. Rooms had been communal in Wisconsin and doors were never shut. As I walked over to the window, I could still feel the sway of the train beneath me, the two nights and three days. I leaned out into the moon world. The unearthly radiance and the strangeness made it like a dream. The farm in Wisconsin with my aunt and uncle and cousins had grown to seem my lot in life and inevitable. I was reluctant to get into the bed, for fear that I should awake.

Hot sun woke me up. I was looking at Soledad, gray-green now against a postcard-blue sky. It could not be early because the air was streaked with wild herb scents brought out by the heat of the sun. As I opened the door, my grandmother passed on her way from her bath. She was still the white eagle I remembered from childhood, her appearance had not altered, but the scale had changed—she was a miniature of herself. Her sudden smallness made me feel protective, and for the first time I realized I belonged to an adult world.

In the breakfast room everything was immaculate and sunny, a great bowl of fruit stood on the table. My grandmother advised me to follow her example and make my breakfast of dates and milk, a delicious combination. She hoped I was not addicted to drinking stimulants the first thing in the morning. She kept tea in the house but she did not approve of it at this time of day. Reassured, she left me.

As I went back through the drawing room, I saw her in the patio, reading a newspaper. An awning had been pulled across the center to make shade. A gardener was moving the sprinkler on the lawn. She looked up as though she had been waiting for me. "I am sorry, but some time ago I arranged to go up the coast on a painting expedition. I thought it better to start as we mean to go on. You may even enjoy a day to yourself to settle down and unpack. And you have a bread-and-butter letter to write."

When the car was there, she called me to hand the folded easel, the paint box and canvas stool to the chauffeur.

At the final click of the door, a release spread through the empty house. With time to spare, time to waste, too restless to sit down or do any one thing, I drifted through the quiet rooms, out to the patio and back to the drawing room. In daylight it was larger than I had thought: the grand piano had its corner and kept to it. Opposite the patio was an arched door of plate glass leading out to a balcony. From it I could see an expanse of the Pacific, smooth at this distance as a looking glass, and like one adazzle with sun. From the dining-room windows on both sides stretched the straight blue horizon above the housetops. I had to force myself back to my own room. Soledad (close in this light as a painting on the wall) did not distract me—it was the ocean which shook me with exaltation. I unlocked my steamer trunk and unpacked.

In my memory it is only this day which passed as though held in check by the tick of the clock. I sat in the patio with a writing pad on my lap, struggling with the draft of my letter. I could write down nothing that sounded like gratitude. I did not feel grateful. Unpleasant pictures presented themselves, a long row of hurting and of what I considered unjust acts. What I could never forget was the time my aunt had called me into her bedroom—which was the usual ritual of a scolding, although this time I could not think of anything I had done—and read me, out of the blue, a matter-of-fact letter from my Uncle John, obviously in answer to complaints about me, saying that there was no reason why I should not be placed in an orphanage. Nothing further had ever been said about orphanages, and I was left wondering at the reason why my aunt had read me that letter. Was it to show how kind she was? That she was standing between me and a fate which could easily be mine? Or was it to remind me that life was a grim affair, not taking into account that that point had been rubbed into me every day since I had come into her household?

I took a fresh sheet of paper and arranged words as one would shift hard separate pebbles into a design. The result was stilted. I copied it out, addressed the envelope and stamped it, and with that final gesture, I dropped the past from my mind and stretched myself out on the chaise longue.

A bell pealed in the honeyed stillness—the doorbell? I opened the front door to strangers—a couple, the man English-dressed and the woman, of the world, with an arrogant dash to her hat—easy, cocksure, smiling. I smiled back.

"Is my mother at home?" the woman said.

They were in the drawing room. "So you have arrived," she said and kissed me on both cheeks. She held me at arm's length, looking at me keenly, fondly. My father had always been her favorite brother. I was very like him, and with those words I knew that she was offering me a place in her heart. She introduced my Uncle Andrew, who had been pacing about, almost stamping his feet, as though he had been driving a long distance in a cramped position and

12

had but a few moments to limber himself. This proved to be exactly the case. They were on their way back from Mexico and were driving straight on to their ranch farther north at Riverside. They couldn't wait. But they were glad, now, that they had stopped. She thrust her arm through mine and together we went out of the door and down the steps. "You and I," she said, "will have to make up for the lost years." They got into a great monster of a car, a Delage, and as they drove off they waved and smiled like old friends.

I do not know why I had not reckoned with my Aunt Augusta. It had not occurred to me that she lived near enough to be part of my life.

My eldest Wisconsin cousin, Laura, had once spent a few months' visit in Aunt Augusta's house. She had started out with misgivings: her aunt had divorced her first husband, and that was wicked in the sight of the Lord and in Laura's sight; her aunt had spent many years in London, an exile, which in itself was suspicious. What Laura found in Riverside confirmed every misgiving: Aunt Augusta powdered her face and probably painted it, she wore earrings. On the evening of her arrival Laura had been confronted with champagne. Naturally she had refused it. Misunderstandings grew; things went from bad to worse; Aunt Augusta ignored Laura's moral stand. Without turning a hair, she smoked cigarettes in front of her niece. Laura had had to write her mother to send for her.

When I was sent to Wisconsin, these tales were still bleeding wounds—Laura had just returned. At first, they had sounded like gibberish; later, I was to realize that it was serious. The moral outlook was Sacred Family Law. The Law condemned the ornaments and trappings of society, and it extended far beyond the fleshpots of the world; literal word-for-word belief in the Bible was exacted. Once, when I happened to mention the name of Darwin under the household roof, I was sent off to bed without my dinner. How my accomplice—because it came about in a discussion with a university professor who had been asked to the house—took the matter, I have no idea.

During the (four gray eternal) years of Wisconsin, Aunt Augusta faded from family talk but not from my mind. There, gradually, as I was thrown again and again against the implacable Law, she became transformed into a secret symbol of enlightenment, the archangel of the other side—my side. To have her appear now, out of nowhere, a vital and active ally, someone I loved on sight, filled my cup to the brim. I walked slowly back to the house not to jog it.

My grandmother did not return exhausted, as I had expected, but in a bustle of high spirits. She handed me her wet canvas to be taken out to the studio, which was a separate building at the end of the garden, opposite the garage. She went ahead quickly on her stick and unlocked the door. It was a large room with a wooden easel in the center and paintings stacked against the walls. I was sent back at once for the other things. My grandmother had thrown off her coat and held out her hands for the paint box. She always cleaned her brushes first thing, she said. She would join me in a minute.

I wandered about the garden looking at the unfamiliar shrubs and trees. One small tree was covered with a strange green fruit; I could not imagine what it was until I saw that one had turned yellow. Lemons! It was as startling

14

as a tree bearing unripe mustard pots. Grandmother came up from behind me and picked the yellow one. The juice was sharper and the lemons kept better if they did not ripen too long on the tree. As we walked toward the house together, she exclaimed with disappointment at having missed Aunt Augusta and Uncle Andrew. At least my day had not been too dull, she said. "Tomorrow, we must launch you into outside activities." In fact she thought she should take me out tonight. After she had rested, we would go to the hotel for dinner.

The road to the hotel was downhill all the way and curved along the side of the sea until we came to a rocky promontory which seemed the edge of the world. Grandmother told the driver to stop, and we got out of the car for a moment. The sun was sliding below the horizon, and with its going the whole sky was lit with pinks and reds.

"We have very dramatic sunsets," Grandmother said.

But I was more caught by the immensity of the horizon and the sound of the waves and the salty spray. I think she saw the exicitement in my face, and was pleased as any hostess is pleased by the success of her arrangements.

The hotel was just behind us. Grandmother said it had been opened recently although it had very cleverly been made to look as though it had stood there forever. It was vast and low and Spanish in style. We went straight into the dining room, which was airy and large. For me the evening was a revelation and a return. Like a water creature who for a long time has been cooped up on dry land and at last is released into smooth water, I slipped into the chair opposite my grandmother, into the rosy light, with the sensation of being back again, in the right place.

A rather roly-poly gay-looking woman in extreme décol-
leté stood in the doorway. I wondered why anyone should
choose to expose so much white flesh when it could be
concealed. "That is Polly Prentiss," Grandmother said, "a
dear. She is the social hostess—whatever that may be—but
nobody is better fitted for it. She can make anyone think
he is enjoying himself. This talent is all the more remarkable in that she comes from a very stiff Boston family."

I noticed that Grandmother did not refuse a small black
coffee at night. By this time, many people had left the
dining room. The social hostess came over to our table and
said that the committee was waiting for my grandmother
in the library. Grandmother said that my arrival had put
the whole affair out of her mind. Polly Prentiss said she
would see me through the evening.

She had to arrange bridge games in the card room, and
on the way through the lounge we met a girl whom Polly
clasped with her other arm; she said she had been looking
for her to make a fourth. She introduced her as a daughter
of a friend of my grandmother, Sonia Randall. Sonia, she
said, had just come back from a holiday in France and
found it difficult to keep her feet on the ground and speak
ordinary English again. Sonia laughed and said that Polly
shouldn't tease. She had black hair and eyes, high coloring
and vivid red lips, which gave her a sparkling foreign look.
She was not even pretty but she had the manner of beauty.

When she heard that I was not playing and that I did
not even know the game, she said if I sat next to her, she
would show me in a few minutes. She had taken lessons
from a professional last winter, and what had she learned?
To shuffle and deal rapidly. Nothing else really mattered,

he had said. Slowness was the deadly sin. In bidding, it was more important to be quick than right. So I sat next to Sonia and watched.

Cards had been taboo in Wisconsin. But before that as a child I had loved card games, and I had played hearts and then whist, so bridge was easy to follow. The bidding was the big difference. By the end of the evening I felt ready to try my hand. Sonia seemed to take it for granted, because she said she would arrange a game with a couple of friends. How long was I staying? In that case, I would be going to school at Miss Cunningham's. So was she. We discovered that we were in the same class.

Grandmother and Sonia's mother came into the card room together. My grandmother looked pleased, and Mrs. Randall said she was, to find that Sonia and I had made each other's acquaintance. When Sonia said she would telephone about the bridge, it was my grandmother who said, "How kind," while I was still wondering if I should have asked her first. And on the way to the car, Grandmother took my arm and said she could not be more delighted; pleasures and sociability were a very necessary part of life. We had come to the car door as she said this, and waiting for her to step in, I faced the sea and the path the moon made, luminous as the reflection of Grandmother's words in my mind.

II

T_{HE} NEXT MORNING was a Thursday. On Monday and Thursday mornings two men from a San Diego firm came to clean the house. My grandmother said she found it wiser to go out while they were there. She couldn't get away from the sound of the vacuum cleaner but the noise was less trying than the silences—it was then that she began to wonder what the men were doing and she would be drawn into watching—so it would end by their giving notice or by her firing them. She had found out that they were all much the same. Now, she went out and left them to it, and the house was as clean or as dirty as it would have been in any case.

This, too, was a marching with the times. One was forced

to it. To most of her friends the world was falling apart; of course the old standards had gone. But she had hope; she saw something new emerging: more chances for more people, better education, broader ideas. Judge Landis—she still kept up her correspondence with him—had opened her eyes to the sound good sense of some of the aspects of this unbridled freedom, this dam which had burst after the war. What did I think of companionate marriage? To her it seemed logical enough. How can young couples know what they are letting themselves in for unless they try it out first?

My grandmother took me into La Playa to show me where the shops and post office were. The shopping center was a short street off the main sea road. It was quiet and leisurely; Grandmother met a great many friends. The shops were small and select and gave a sense of opulence. Grandmother said she bought what she could in La Playa to encourage local trading, even if it meant paying slightly more. We dawdled through the fruit and vegetable shops, choosing here and there. I put the parcels in the car and waited for Grandmother, who had stopped to speak to a tall white-haired man in plus fours and thick-soled golf shoes. We went on down the street to a shop where Grandmother had ordered an evening dress. The owner, Grandmother said, was one of a number of young widows of good family who, when they found out that they could not manage after the war on the incomes left them, had come to La Playa and had set themselves up in small businesses. It gave a special feeling to the place. It made La Playa a friendly close community. Before we left the shop, Grandmother had chosen me a couple of tennis dresses and a simple silk afternoon dress. Two doors farther down I was fitted with tennis shoes.

Because she had arranged for me to have a tennis lesson at the club on Thursday afternoons, as it was then that she had friends in to play chamber music—two violins and a cello. She would leave the patio door into the corridor unlocked so I need not come in through the drawing room. Probably I would want more than one lesson in a week; the other days I should decide for myself.

I was ahead of time at the tennis club. The secretary took me to the bleachers and pointed out a woman with short blond hair, playing in mixed doubles: she was the instructor. It was a sharp swift game. The ball seemed drawn to the rackets, which met it, effortlessly, with a full satisfying plonk.

When the game broke up, the instructor came over to me. She was brown as a nut and finely muscular, very matter-of-fact, no nonsense. She showed me at once why it was I poked at a serve instead of coming down on top of it. She made me throw the balls up high and straight and hit them as though the racket were a stone on the end of a string. We settled for another lesson on Mondays, and I walked home with a singing happiness. What a wonderful theory that pleasures were a necessary part of life.

As far back as I could remember, my greatest passion had been for water and swimming. Now, the first chance I had, I put on my bathing suit and walked down the hill to the bathing beach. It was not far from the house—five minutes downhill, eight to climb back—a sandy cove at the foot of a cliff, reached by wooden steps. Looking down over the top railing, I saw some bathers grouped on the sand and a few small capped heads sprinkled in the clear transparent water. The cove was curved behind a headland which protected it from the open sea; the waves that came in here were gently cradled.

I was glad I did not know anybody; I slipped into the water the moment I got to it. Waist-deep I dived and swam with my eyes open to the cool greenness. Weightless, fluid, I glided. Up for breath and under again. Far out alone I turned on my back, suspended, rocked, I stared into the sky. In pleasure suddenly downward, I swam into the cold dark with a glint of fish. Salt water—the sea—was a new live element, as different from plain water as unexpected wings.

Within a week a new life had opened out like a fan. I went with Sonia to play bridge with two girls she knew, Janet and Mary Manning. Mrs. Manning was another of the widows on their own; she had a real estate agency on the top floor of her house, which was ground floor from the street. The house had been built downward on a hill so that the room where we played opened onto a narrow graveled terrace below street level. From the front door we saw only the two eucalyptus trees and a view between them of the sea. We always played at the Mannings' house because when Mrs. Manning went out, she switched the office telephone downstairs and Janet took the messages. Except for the occasional ringing of the telephone, we were cut off and tucked away; no one, no grownup, came in to interrupt.

Janet had already graduated from Miss Cunningham's and felt herself to be out in the world. She sat at the card table with a cigarette smoking on an ashtray and was rather offhand with us because we were Mary's age and still at school. She said we would have to play for some sort of stakes; otherwise she couldn't keep her mind on the game. She nodded Mary into the place opposite her. The table lamps were lit, and when Sonia said what a snug sense of wickedness one got from turning day into night, Janet said, "It's a dark room. Cut for deal."

I was delighted to have Sonia for a partner: she played extremely well, she drew lucky hands, and she was an aggressive bidder. "No, not a mind reader," she said when I accused her of that. *"You* indicated your strength quite properly."

I had been poring over a bridge manual at the public library, but it was the last thing I would have admitted to anyone as sure of herself as Sonia. Now if it were necessary, I took the reins in my own hands and played the game myself. I discovered the exhilaration of the give-and-take, of the interchange with a quick responsive partner. I felt a mind reader myself, and saw what fun it was.

Bridge was the cornerstone and the beginning of my friendship for Sonia; the rest followed rapidly and naturally. Wherever I went with Grandmother, there was Sonia and her mother. Generally we two were the only ones of our age at these gatherings. Grandmother liked Mrs. Randall and approved of Sonia, and when she discovered that Sonia's presence turned our family reticence into a party, she began to ask her to join our dinners at the hotel.

One of Sonia's first gestures of friendship was to lend me *The Picture of Dorian Gray.* I should read it now, she said. Sixteen was the perfect age. It was plain that she had, and that she was not above practicing what she preached.

I found it a sign of confidence that she did this, because she was putting into my hands the model and key to her style of conversation (not to Grandmother, of course).

My grandmother, too, was handing on books to read, nothing very particular, simply the novels which she had been reading and had liked: by Christopher Morley or Thornton Wilder or Aldous Huxley. She made a point of discussing them with me afterwards. I think it was a way of trying to find out what I was like and what I thought about things. I came to realize that she was puzzled. The fact that I had not wanted to stay on in Wisconsin was incomprehensible to her. Did I crave excitement? she asked. She went out of her way to explain that life in La Playa was very simple.

What seemed to reassure her to some degree was my delight in everything round me—the very things she had called simple—the sea, the sun, the sun-baked land. And even Sonia, although, goodness knows, she was not simple.

My Aunt Augusta wrote that she and Uncle Andrew were anxious that I should come and stay with them. I went from San Diego by train, and, like my Wisconsin cousin Laura, I went with misgivings. But mine were for my own shortcomings. I felt that I was going to be found out, found inadequate; I was convinced that Aunt Augusta would think me unworthy of my father. My grandmother had brought up another worry by telling me how talented and accomplished my Uncle Andrew was—a scientist and an artist, brilliant in both fields. I should not lose any opportunity of talking to him. By the time I had caught the train,

I prayed that I would never find myself alone with my uncle.

Arrived at Riverside, I was swept into embraces and along the platform into the car. They were both so pleased and gay that I was drawn into it. And talking was not difficult because I sat in the back with Aunt Augusta, who asked about her mother and told me about their orange ranch in the same breath. Orange trees stretched on both sides of the road. Aunt Augusta said it was very exacting to look after the trees during the months of frost. Andrew had installed a thermostatic gauge to light the smudge pots. And now that he had this device which should have made it possible for him to sleep at night, he did not trust it. He had to be on the spot to see that it worked. He was not young enough to jump out of bed whenever the night was cold. She had put her foot down and Andrew had been a lamb. He had bought her a house near Laguna, which they were going to use as a summer house until they found a good buyer for the ranch. So they would be near us next summer, perhaps before. She hadn't told her mother yet. It had just happened.

We drove under the spread of shade trees and stopped at a white portico. An Airedale ran up to meet us, wagging his whole body in greeting. Aunt Augusta said his name was Seal because he was happiest in water.

"Like me," I said.

"And like your father. When he was a boy, he used to go down to the lake and swim in his sleep."

The hall was wide and paneled in a dark wood. The ceilings were high. Aunt Augusta said, "Not one's idea of a California house"—as indeed it wasn't. Copied, lock, stock

24

and barrel, from England. This particular region round Riverside had always been something of an English colony.

When I went downstairs to dinner, Aunt Augusta was sitting on the divan facing a log fire and Uncle Andrew stood with his back to it. They were holding cocktails and laughing. My aunt patted the divan next to her, and as soon as I sat down, Seal came over and lay with his head on my foot. Aunt Augusta said that was to show his approval. "Seal is teetotal like your cousin Laura. But unlike her, he forgives us."

"So you knew?"

A maid came to the door, Andrew took Augusta's empty glass and we walked into the dining room. The table was both stately and pretty in the candlelight, with scarlet flowers flat as water lilies on a dark pool which reflected back the candelabras and the tall-stemmed wine glasses.

We had coffee in the drawing room and I was handed a cup as a matter of course. Aunt Augusta said that Andrew was reading *Lord Jim* aloud to her. Would I mind if they went on with it?

Uncle Andrew read clearly and without embarrassing emphasis. I watched the fire and sometimes looked up at Aunt Augusta, whose profile was lit by the lamp at her side. I recognized the family features, but here they were more delicately proportioned and sweetly cut. A face from a golden age. She caught my look and smiled.

In the days that followed, Augusta and I spent the whole time talking. Talking as she snipped flowers and dropped them into the basket I held. Talking as I followed her through the house, moving a chair, patting a cushion; sitting under the trees sewing. She told me about her past, about her first husband, her life in England, how she met Andrew, how he had proposed when they were stuck in the mud on the Thames. The terrible decision about a divorce; divorce was beyond the pale at that time.

Augusta was doing exactly what she had promised: she was making up for lost years. With breathtaking candor, she walked through barriers. It was strange country to me; I had never exchanged confidences before. She did not put questions or press for answers; talking with her was like the light and shadow under a tree when a breeze is blowing, flashes of understanding.

Laura's visit had cleared the way for me; there was no need to explain Wisconsin. A defeating experience, Augusta had called her visit. She was curious to know if the younger cousins were like her. Laura was more militant, I supposed, but the pattern was the same. The outside world did not touch them. For miles, there were no friends, no neighbors except foreign-born farmers. The Wisconsin farm was a feudal court, in a nutshell.

Augusta said her mother had no idea, of course, and no one could tell her. She idealized the farm.

Half past four was the hour for tea, and we had it under the trees near the tennis court. Guests would appear by magic along the path from the front driveway: the Trevelyans, the Phillipses, the Whiteheads. They brought their tennis rackets, or their bathing suits for a swim in the reservoir. It was casual and seemed a habit of long standing. Augusta held court round the tea table while anyone who felt like it made up a set. The Trevelyan twins, girls about my age, came one day especially to play tennis with me.

When I had fetched my racket from the house, they both stood up. They could only play doubles, they said. Andrew laughed and said that they were more formidable than Shiva: they had four legs as well as the arms. In the name of family honor, he would join me. I was still in awe of Andrew and rather terrified of him. But he kept up a teasing comment with the twins; if I missed a ball, he was behind me to get it. He was so natural and good-natured that at the end of three sets, we were as easy as friends.

Andrew was a big man with blunt features, level gray eyes and a pale full face. He looked quite handsome when he wore a hat, which he did more often than most men. His hair was all right at the sides; it was only on top that it was bare and shone in the lamplight. So when he read aloud in the evenings, I found myself looking more at his hands. They were remarkably conscious hands and immaculate. One morning I said to Augusta—because she seemed to enjoy talking about Andrew—that his hands were like a surgeon's, so scrubbed. Augusta had said, yes of course, perhaps because he was a scientist. After a pause she said, nonsense, it was because he was a gentleman. She spoke as though one were of as much weight as the other.

On my last evening I was reminded of this when Andrew handed me the small delicate coffee cup, and I felt a pang at the loss of this happy world. Augusta, quick to guess thoughts, said that we would have all day tomorrow. She and Andrew had decided to drive me back. She felt she must see her mother before the winter settled down.

Andrew said that they had let time slide past without saying what they had meant to: that if I found things too much, I could always rely on them. I should let Augusta know.

Augusta laughed and said that Andrew was so tactful that he hadn't been very explicit. They were both worried about how I would get on with my grandmother. Did I realize that her own children had always been petrified by her?

"Augusta stubs out her cigarette," Andrew said, "when she hears her mother's voice on the telephone."

"She has no human failings; that is so terrifying," Augusta said.

Andrew gave her an amused glance.

I was used to her, I said. I had known her quite a long time, ever since I was four.

Augusta pointed out that her own children had known her as long.

It seemed to me that being a grandchild made a difference. She did not expect as much from a grandchild—it was too diluted. And that worked both ways.

Augusta kissed me good night. "Remember, diluted or not, if anything goes wrong, you can always come to us."

We set off at ten with a picnic lunch packed in the back. Andrew drove their favorite way, through the mountains of the back country. The road was not as wide or as smooth as the coast road, but they liked it because it was deserted. We sailed along, down, round, and up again. Speed and air and open sky soon made us hungry. We stopped in a valley green with live oaks and grass on the bank of a river. A California river, Andrew said, so there would be no water in it at this time of year. We sat on grass in the shade and Andrew boasted that he had produced the only trees and grass between Riverside and La Playa. It was true: the mountains had been treeless, rocky, or covered with scrub.

Augusta had poured from a thermos flask a pale straw-colored liquid into two fine glasses, which at once misted over with cold. Then came sandwiches of egg and anchovy, cream cheese and chives, slices of ham between thin rye bread. Hot coffee from another flask. Augusta and Andrew lit cigarettes and told me the story of why this place had been called the Lion's Grove. The first time they had seen it, they had driven past, not believing their eyes. Then they had backed up. Under one of the trees stood a cage on a trailer, and inside was a dusty old lion sound asleep. No other sign of life.

Calling it the Lion's Grove, Augusta said, made them think of the early Italian paintings of the lion with the thorn in his paw, waiting his turn to be healed, lying outsized— as big as the trees. And speaking of lions waiting, Augusta said, we must be on our way.

Grandmother was a mild and gentle figure in the doorway, smiling welcome. Her face had taken on a tinge of pink, and something in her expression had shifted so that one saw, hinted, the charm she must have had as a young woman. She embraced Augusta and led us through the drawing room, which seemed doll-sized after the ranch, and out into the patio where she said Andrew would be more comfortable because he could smoke.

The news about the house at Laguna was like a spark on dry twigs; Grandmother exclaimed with joy and everyone began speaking at once. A hubbub roared up and then exhausted itself. Finally we sat down and Grandmother poured tea.

I marveled at Augusta's relaxed and affectionate way with her mother. I would have thought she was being entirely natural if it had not been for the absence of her cigarette. At the ranch I had seen that smoking was as necessary to her as breathing. Knowing the backstage secrets, I was able to see what witchery smooth manners and control can bring about. I was filled with admiration. I felt I was seeing how the world ticked, how one could hold it and make it tick.

III

WHENEVER MY GRANDMOTHER had a serious matter to discuss with me—a matter concerning my life or my future—she did not broach it in broad daylight or face to face in the well-lit drawing room but out under the stars in the patio, so that with the years this enclosure in the sweet dark nights, my grandmother's half-obscured figure—the advocate and judge—constituted for me a sort of moral countinghouse, the place and condition of conscience.

In the early days my life was the future, an innocent topic, compounded of supposition and conjecture for which I could not be held answerable, and so I listened as to a tale. To me at that time it was all vague and far away. Sometimes my grandmother predicted a life of hardship. I might easily have been alarmed. But as she went on, I saw that she was speaking of the human condition and the momentum of progress. At other times she was reassuring: barring a world cataclysm, and if I remained as reasonable as I seemed, I would have enough and more than enough. I believe she meant money. The warnings and the assurances washed over me. I did not take any of it in. My grandmother was talking about when I was *old*, and that was a time beyond imagination.

One night before school started Grandmother did touch upon the present. She told me that under no circumstances would she allow me to go to Miss Cunningham's as a boarder. Although that arrangement would have suited her better, she did not believe in a cloistered life for the young. She spoke as though to quell opposition.

I dreaded the first day. Miss Cunningham's looked formidable. I was familiar enough with the outside. On the way to Sonia's house, I passed that block-long sweep of blinding white architecture, a severe, noncommittal front. I was to learn that that was the side of school which we inmates became unconscious of, much as we did the features of our own faces.

On the fateful day, the worst part was walking through the side gate and facing the quadrangle. In the mid-distance, like bees in swarm, was a conglomeration of girls in school uniform, and beyond them a chapel and covered arcades. As I came nearer, I heard the hum of talk. Sonia and Mary Manning detached themselves and walked forward to meet me. From that moment, school swallowed me and my day-lit hours as completely as the whale did Jonah until I

32

was spewed out two years later amid fanfares, speeches, and school prizes.

Curriculum and timetable were designed to prevent a single idle moment for mischief. Intervals between classes were just long enough to cover the distance between classrooms. The courses were not easy, and each teacher assigned homework as though her subject were the important one of the school. Miss Cunningham's served three main purposes: it was accredited to the big women's colleges in the East, it was a finishing school, last and far from least—it was a *safe* place for a girl. And so the serious intelligent girls from the West Coast came, and the beautiful and the high-spirited ones who were much too much of a handful at home, those with the ambition to be finished, and some Easterners whose parents wintered at Pasadena. This odd assortment was welded by continuous motion: chapel, classes, study hall, classes, games, chapel. I thought of Miss Cunningham's when, in Hawaii, I watched the dark crushed sugar-cane juices flow into the centrifugal machine which whirled them round and whirled them out, pure white crystals.

Mornings, on the way to school, I was usually in a hurry and without thought except for the lateness; and yet in looking back, these early walks form the one unshattered memory of that time. I went by the shortcut, up over the lower slope of the mountain, across the not yet built-up fields of scrub and herb, aromatic underfoot; above me always the sun in a limitless blue sky, Soledad crouched and sleeping, and to my right the morning sea bright as a silver tray and fair as a promise. I felt at the brink, on the verge of everything. Everything, anything, was possible.

I can smile now at my boundless confidence. I was intimidated in no way by my own ignorance. I attempted things I would not have dreamed of a few years later. In chemistry class I figured out on paper a way of making gasoline from coal. Miss Fletcher, the science mistress, was delighted to find a pupil who took more than a cursory interest in lessons. I do not remember that she was excited by my findings but she asked to see my computations. She kept them overnight and when she gave them back after class, she said I did not seem to have made a mistake. At one point she thought I might need a catalytic agent, probably platinum. If I wanted to give it a tryout, she would help me rig up an apparatus on a Saturday morning. At the second attempt the experiment did come out all right. We needed the platinum—fortunately the science department had some—and a certain amount of heat. While we were at work, Miss Fletcher had lectured on each step as though it were an ordinary lesson, and at the end she told me to draw the apparatus and put it with the data in a notebook. It would be interesting to keep. I did not say that I planned to find out if the process would be worth developing commercially.

I was teased by the few friends who knew I had put in extra time on chemistry. The English mistress bombarded me with difficult questions in class, and when she caught me out, remarked that I was neglecting Donne for stinkpots. My grandmother half listened and said it was remarkable what was taught in school nowadays. Uncle Andrew wrote that if I wanted to get anywhere in *that* field, I should put my mind to the breaking up of the atom. Augusta was silent; Sonia quite without interest.

Sonia's attitude to school was carefree. To her, it was marking time; she had no wish to go to college; she didn't care what grades she got as long as she passed. She would rather say she hadn't studied than bother to recite. Only in moments of crisis did she show her mettle. Like the time in Latin class when Miss Cunningham had come in and Miss Waltham had already asked Sonia to translate a passage of Virgil and had been told that she had not studied it. Pointedly, Miss Waltham called on Sonia again. Straight off, as though it were a lively novel, Sonia began to read. I was sitting next to her and saw that she had no crib. She read fast and interestingly. Everybody's mouth dropped open. Miss Waltham was too startled to stop her. She had long passed the day's lesson when the bell rang.

Occasions like this bound me to Sonia. In Wisconsin I had been a grind at study—there had been nothing else to do. I had got used to making straight A's, and when you get used to a thing like that, it is as insidious as being used to a large income: you feel you cannot do with less. To keep up with my studies, and at the same time to make Sonia feel that I was not boringly serious, I had to learn to be quick and concentrated. It was very good practice.

When my grandmother or Mrs. Randall left La Playa for short excursions—my grandmother to Pasadena or to Palm Springs to paint, Mrs. Randall farther afield to San Francisco—they arranged between them that I stay in Sonia's house or she in mine. Sonia and I preferred her house. It was nearer school, and it was more exciting. Sonia and her sister (who was away at college) had a wing of the house to themselves. It was luxurious and elaborate with low dressing tables, pale silk bed covers and curtains, and in the bathroom a tub sunk like a pool. I thought it must be very gratifying to have had rooms designed and built for oneself. And Sonia's pale pink satin dressing gown, her velvet mules and scented bath steam made her world all the more agreeable to share.

Left on our own, Sonia and I played a good deal of bridge in the evenings with the Manning girls, and if Mary went off to study, Mrs. Manning took her place. When our families were at home, we went back to dining at the hotel. Throughout the winter we went every Tuesday night to the Little Opera.

The Little Opera was the idea of a young Russian protégé of Polly Prentiss. He was the designer, the producer, and the director. In fact, he was everything. He had built an exact duplicate of the stage and side boxes of the Metropolitan Opera House, and the same operas were given as in New York. He had the complete gramophone recordings of them all. Theater seats had been arranged in a large room facing the stage. When the lights were out and the curtains went up, there would be a gasp of pleasure. The décor was always imaginative and striking. There was no attempt with puppets, only the setting and the music. The Russian, unobtrusively and with few words, kept us informed of the action on the stage. While he spoke, the records were changed; I was never conscious of hitches or of the mechanism behind scenes.

It was a wonderful way of becoming familiar with a great many operas, though for me forever afterwards it spoiled the real thing. Singers actually *on* the stage distracted my attention.

Polly Prentiss had launched the Little Opera, and the social world of La Playa rallied to it. Each performance was an occasion and meant full dress for everybody except Sonia and me who were considered too young. During the interval before the last act, we withdrew to another room for conversation and refreshments. Sonia and I handed round the sandwiches, and were treated like daughters of the house, with pleasant remarks from the women and elaborate gallantry from the men.

The fact that I spent so many evenings in my grandmother's company, on her own ground and with her friends, gave us a great many things to talk about. It almost seemed as though the difference in age had dropped away. We actually chatted. We were almost *chums* (if this preposterous word could ever be associated with my grandmother, it might describe the ease between us which, until now, had seemed equally preposterous).

When the Christmas holidays came round and talk of a ball at the hotel, my grandmother did not hesitate; she bought me what she called a pretty and youthful evening dress and invited an old friend of hers, Mr. Fowler, and his son who was my age to dine that night at the hotel. Mr. Fowler and I had become cronies at the Little Opera, and so at dinner we fell into easy talk. His son Edward dismissed me with a glance and turned his full attention to my grandmother. What was her opinion of the Berkeley theory? "It is a stage some young men go through," Mr. Fowler said to me. "He is awe-struck by his own mind."

Sonia and her sister were sitting at a corner table with two handsome young men I had never seen before. The orchestra had been playing for some time and almost every-

37

one went out to dance between courses. Mr. Fowler told me an amusing story about his cigarette lighter. It snapped alight at the merest touch. And whenever he wore tails, it kept him up to the mark. If he relaxed and leaned back, he burst into flames. Later on, between dances, he showed me where he had to keep the lighter, the one and only pocket in his tailcoat.

When we moved to the ballroom, Edward said he never danced and went on talking to Grandmother. I was perfectly happy that he didn't. I enjoyed dancing with Mr. Fowler because he liked it, too, and had a natural sense of rhythm.

The next day Grandmother said, didn't I think Edward Fowler a very pleasant boy?

Sonia came round to talk about the ball. I said that she had looked ravishing. *He* was a Yale man, she said. I pleased her by saying how good-looking he was. She took up this theme herself until she was stopped in the middle of a sentence by a sudden thought. She knew, she said, that Mr. Fowler was a dear, but didn't I find him a waste of time? "You can't marry a Mr. Fowler."

Sonia's point of view did not upset me in the least. I knew she had made very definite plans for her own future (which was practically on top of her because it would start as soon as she left Miss Cunningham's): she was going to marry the first good-looking eligible man from the Eastern seaboard, naturally a Yale or Harvard or Princeton man. She hated California. It was too hot and too far away. She liked snow, log fires, sleighs, the contrast of seasons, spring flowers, green grass, summer. And a large house of her own.

My grandmother wanted to be in Pasadena over the new

year, and as she thought a change would be good for me, we drove up together and she sent me on in the car to Riverside. I was to have a few days at the ranch and I was looking forward to being with Augusta again, to the long talks and quiet evenings.

After a joyful welcome, Augusta told me how pleased she was that this time she could offer me all sorts of gay parties. The Trevelyans had especially asked that I come to a dance they were giving. The Whiteheads wanted me for a luncheon party. And before I left, she and Andrew would give a bridge and supper party for the young set—they were all at home now. I may have looked my dismay, because she quickly said, "Don't tell me you are a wallflower!" I managed to get out that I preferred to be with her to anything in the world. Her arm tightened round me, "You are being a little bit of a goose," she said.

If Sonia could have seen me at the Trevelyan dance, she would not have thought it a waste of time. The men were all young and handsome. Everybody there was a cousin or a near cousin; they shared a common past and put up a common front, conversation came out only as bursts of tribal jokes. I soon got the impression that I was being subjected to some sort of schoolroom rag. I subsided and just danced. Things went better from then on. Apparently I had passed whatever test they had put me through, because when I went to the luncheon party, they went out of their way to be agreeable. I was glad, not so much for myself but because their parents were friends of Augusta's, and it would all come back to her in the end. I would have slain dragons for Augusta.

On my last morning while we were waiting for Grandmother's car to pick me up, and I had gone into the butler's pantry with Augusta to look for a large vase, unexpectedly —I think she was as surprised as I was—Augusta burst into tears and put her head on my shoulder. She was so worried about Andrew; he was much older than she was, did I know? His heart wasn't good, either. I tried to comfort her. She admitted she had no reason—no more than usual—to make her worry. Was it a premonition or was she just tired? She dried her tears and went on with her flowers. She said they thought they had found a serious buyer for the ranch. What a relief it was going to be to know that Andrew would not have to work so hard.

Alone in the back of the car on the way to Pasadena, I gave myself up to thinking about Augusta. The shock of seeing her cry—of seeing anyone grown up cry—had begun to wear off, and in its place my heart leapt. Augusta trusted me. Crying in front of someone was a sign of trust. I had not done it since I was a baby. It was a last barrier.

When Augusta had kissed me goodbye, I had sensed in her a new acceptance, as though she had just opened the door and let me in, and that was curious because from the first moment of meeting her, she had made me feel that we were on the same side of the door; curious how one can keep on going through the same door and coming into the same place, but more deeply in.

IV

I N THE WINTER TERM the seals never stopped barking.
From the sea their cries rang out over La Playa and pene-
trated into the innermost classroom. Like a primitive drum-
beat, this ceaseless repetition affected the girls at school in
different ways—some went with it and threw themselves
into work; some were provoked into snapping with irritation.
Sonia had her own solution: she went off to San Francisco
with her mother for ten days.

After school I went down to the rocks to watch the seals
sporting in the waves like children let loose on holiday. To
me their cries were exultant and exciting. My spirits soared
and were suspended. I was on the heights and, up there,
it seemed that something significant ought to happen. All

I found was Edward Fowler prowling in the hotel library after dinner. He was at a loose end, he said. He had finished his school in the East, and his father thought he was too young to start college. He opened the book he had his thumb in. Did I know, he said, that harmony had appeared in the world about the time of Christ?

That was a shadow of what I was waiting for. I realized then that I wanted nothing less than to understand the connection between everything—love, life, music, writing —impulse and creation. I couldn't very well say that to a stick like Edward. I was looking for something to read, I said. Not a novel, and nothing dry. Something to throw a new light on things. He reached up and handed me a small book called *An Experiment with Time*.

I took the book home and read it at a gulp. It was a theory after my own heart. Why shouldn't we be able to see the future as well as the past? I didn't feel any limitations to my own powers; surely anything I tried I could do.

Half the time Edward mocked my credulity; half the time he fed the fires. He kept me supplied with theoretical books on the fourth dimension. Afterwards, he would tease me—was it *time*? Or did I believe in the genius of Lewis Carroll—that it was all Through-the-Looking-Glass, that glucose was the fourth dimension of sugar? And what about Einstein? How fast did a fly fly when it flew in a moving train? What of the curvature of space?

With Sonia away, Edward often sat with us after dinner. My grandmother was not as soft a prey as I was. On the one occasion that Edward began to speculate on the common denominator of the arts (and I sat drinking it in), she cut him short. Music was music, and painting, painting; and each was distinct and totally different. For days afterwards, Grandmother bristled. Edward Fowler might be a pleasant young man but he did not keep his feet on the ground. I thought no purpose would be served if I said that I was floating about, just as high.

Sonia came back full of the wonders of San Francisco. It was almost as good as going East. It was frosty and bracing and the people were civilized. They had manners and wit. "Living in a hot climate makes people dull," she said. "Take the South Sea Islanders; then look at the English."

I noticed that she had begun to collect theories, too, but they were all of a practical nature. She told me about her theory of agreement. As I knew, her mother was always accusing her of being lazy and unpunctual (punctuality is the thief of time). She had discovered that it took the wind out of her mother's sails if she agreed *and went one better*. She would say, "Yes, *terribly* lazy," or "*Frightfully* unpunctual." Her mother purred. Later on, I tried this out myself when my grandmother reproved me for being in too much of a rush. It worked wonders. She said I was becoming less of a child and more of a companion.

Most of Sonia's theories were of no use to me. *If you are not a classical beauty, exaggerate your peculiarities* she was putting into practice as hard as she could. She began wearing scarlet and dark reds to bring out her coloring. When I asked if I had any peculiarities, she said, "None."

My grandmother was the wisest person I knew, but she did not drop many hints. Her great standby at that time was *Everything in life has to be paid for*. It seemed a little early for me to do much about this. To be on the safe side,

I resolved to work harder, think harder, exert myself more. It was one kind of payment, the only kind within my reach. I felt I ought to build up a credit on a bill which would run high.

"A penny for your thoughts," Sonia said. "You haven't said an amusing word since I've come back. You've been spending too much time with Edward Fowler." Sonia and Edward did not like each other. She thought he was ugly and a pretentious bore; he resented her manner and thought her frivolous. They were barely polite and fled from each other. I was just as glad they did; it would have been impossible to talk to them both at once—they didn't have a single idea in common.

If they were both at the hotel and I had to choose between them, I naturally chose Sonia. We would play bridge, which Edward didn't. He would go off in a corner and play chess with his father or work out problems by himself from a book. His two hobbies were chess and the stock market. He always carried about with him a black notebook in which he recorded all his dealings. More than a year ago he had invested five thousand dollars (imaginary) and with this he had bought and sold and played on margin. I tried to follow all the things he said he did. What was clear was that he had made a lot of money. He already controlled about fifty thousand dollars' worth of stocks and shares. From the way he talked about it, anyone would have thought he had been making real money.

I asked him what he was going to do when he had made millions, and he looked a shade saddened as though he had often, in his own mind, faced that question. "When that happens," he said, "operating is pretty much of a certainty. In the end it becomes a dope's game—as what doesn't, if you are successful?"

Juanito, who was Grandmother's gardener-chauffeur, had given me driving lessons. Driving a car came easily to me. It was a simple matter in California at that time to get a driving license—I was seventeen, I did not suffer from weak eyes or fits—it was as simple as that. My grandmother had wanted me to be able to drive because she hated to keep a menial hanging about the streets in the dark with nothing to do but wait. It was only recently that this had begun to bother her. Because she hated to be kept waiting herself, her imagination and heart had been struck by the line of cars outside the hotel and by the men who had been lounging there for hours. She didn't mind a bit asking me to fetch her after a late evening; she knew I never went to bed early. So, now, I was put in charge of her evening transport.

My grandmother had phenomenal energy and wide interests. She worked on committees and she worked alone; she worked on civic and public matters and on anything that had to do with the arts, exhibitions and concerts; she helped to launch new artists and she kept up with her own painting and playing. Recently she had joined a life class, which was held every Monday night in the Women's Club building. She had joined, she said, because she felt her drawing was getting rusty.

One Monday night when I had left Grandmother at the Women's Club, I did not feel like going back home to study, so I drove on down to the hotel to see if Sonia was there. The card room was deserted except for Edward bent

45

over his chessboard. He asked me to sit down, and I thought I was in for a session on the stock market. (I was safe from chess; Edward maintained that no woman had that kind of a mind.)

He fiddled with the chessmen, and I was getting bored when he asked what I felt about going to college. I said I hadn't even thought about it yet.

He said he was beginning to get cold feet.

If I had been in Edward's shoes, I would have had cold feet, too. You couldn't look at him without wanting to laugh. He was a comedy figure: his ears stuck out and his spectacles were like goldfish bowls. When he walked into a room, you expected him to knock something over. By now I was certain that he was quite unaware of the impression he gave. It was this that made me truly sorry for him.

The other college men would be so much older and more experienced, he said.

He looked morosely round at the empty half-dimmed card room, and I thought if he would only get out and play tennis or swim, he could get himself into better shape.

"It *is* gloomy here," he said. "Can't we go for a ride?"

I said that there was nowhere to go.

"Please," he said.

I felt it in my bones then that Edward was jockeying himself, much against his own nature, toward his idea of experience. Probably he would try to kiss me. Probably it would be embarrassing, but I did not think it would last long.

I was not surprised when he asked me to turn up to the golf course. I parked not far from the clubhouse; up here it was pitch-dark, cold, and windy. Edward did not make a move but went on sitting bolt upright in his corner. Presently, he said that he wanted me to do something for him. He would greatly appreciate it because it was essential to him before he went to college. Would I undress and stand for a minute in the headlights; he had never seen a naked woman.

I was taken aback and speechless. When words came, I was merely cross. On a night like this? In the cold? The least he could do was to wait for summer!

I switched on the dashboard and looked at my watch. There was still three-quarters of an hour to wait (what a fool I was!), three-quarters of an hour of all that Edward wanted, visible now at the Women's Club. I whirled the car round and we tore down the mountain. I did not tell Edward where we were going; I rather hoped that the surprise would give him a fright. He did balk outside the Club, but that was because the building looked dark. I got him firmly by the hand. When I opened the door to the big back room, into the blaze of light, in front of us stood the nude on the platform. Edward did not turn a hair. He said "Thanks" quickly under his breath, and walked over to where Grandmother had her easel.

Not long afterwards, Mr. Fowler asked what I had done to Edward. He spoke of me as the only sensible and clever girl he had ever met.

V

My grandmother was pleased that the Jay Hamiltons were coming to La Playa for the Easter holidays. The Hamiltons had always been important to our family. Old Mrs. Hamilton was my grandmother's dearest friend; Jay had been my father's, and now he was to bring his daughter Camilla to La Playa. She was home from being finished in the East. I had not seen her since the few times we had met at children's parties in Evanston, Illinois. I could not remember what she was like, only that we used to hide from the other children when the parties were at her house. I remembered the excitement of being singled out.

Uncle Jay was a different matter; we were *old* friends, he had often been at our house when I was a child. He held an almost mysterious place in my life then because of our names. My name wasn't really Jay, but I was called that even though I had turned out to be a girl. A name means a lot to a child, and the fact that Uncle Jay and I shared the same one was a bond between us. At my father's death I had lost my childhood name, and since that time I had not seen Uncle Jay. I wondered what he would do, now that no one called me that. He said, "Hello, Jay." My grandmother winced but she did not say a word. The bond still held.

Camilla was a very quiet girl—pale, blond, and small-boned—fragile and reserved like her mother. She had been beautifully finished: not a hair out of place, not a scratch on her narrow high-heeled shoes, she was dressed in wispy silk and on chilly evenings wrapped in summer ermine. She sat in the Rolls, she strolled from her room to the hotel dining room; that seemed the limit of her activity.

I turned my whole attention to Uncle Jay; it was what he was used to. He was bursting with enthusiasms and he liked to share them. He liked an active response; in fact, he expected the other person to grab the chance to carry them out. All the better if a little courage was needed. That is what he admired—that, with a dash of bravado. I came to understand that was what he had admired in my father. Now he threw my father's mantle on my shoulders and expected me to be like him. I was flattered and of course I played up.

The first time we went across the border into Mexico, he took me to the casino and insisted that I try my hand. There was no question of my gambling away a fortune; I had only five dollars with me. But Jay saw to it that each hand I

49

played was a high risk. He stood at my elbow and bet on my play—one hundred, two hundred, five hundred dollars. I had beginner's luck, a crowd gathered to watch, the croupier was changed. My luck held; it went on so long that Jay lost interest.

Mrs. Hamilton and Camilla were waiting for us in the car. Seeing them there so still and quiet, I realized that they had not even got out. That flamboyant casino meant no more to them than the discomfort of being jostled by the crowds. Gambling did not interest Camilla because money didn't; she had more of it than she knew what to do with.

I spent all my time with the Hamiltons, and although Camilla and I did not talk much, I saw that my first impressions had been hasty. She adored her father and I could see that she longed to show him that she could stand up to the things he did. The trouble was that her physique let her down.

It was Camilla who took her father up when he talked about deep-sea fishing. He arranged a day of it especially for her, but before we had left the jetty ten minutes, the smell of the gasoline and the movement of the boat made it necessary to turn about and take her back.

So once again we swept out to the open sea. A fisherman played out a line for me and handed me the big reel to hold. At that instant my line whizzed out so fast that the skin was burned off my thumb. "Give him line." "Wind it in." The fisherman stood at my side and told me what to do, step by step, minute by minute. There was excitement in the feel of the fish on the line. When he turned in a run, he felt like a wild horse. After a long time (Jay said an hour) the fish jumped high out of the sea quite near the boat. The fisherman said that that should be his last trick; he was tiring. At last I had him in close and the man gaffed him, and there he was, in the bottom of the boat, over fifty pounds of fish—a yellowtail, the man said—and good to eat.

After that first big one, we ran into shoals of barracuda. They did not have the weight or the strength to put up a big fight. We pulled them in until the bottom of the boat was strewn with them and Jay got bored with fish. He proposed that we throw the aquaplane out and that I ride it in. The shore was a faint line in the distance, and I had always heard that barracuda were worse man-eaters than sharks. Jay knew that I had never been on a board. So this was another daredevil challenge! I knew that I couldn't back out.

The board and I went into the water at the same time; better that than having to swim through the barracuda; I lay on it and tried not to think of the blackness under me. The boat was a long time in taking up the tension. As we gathered speed, I stood up, resolved that nothing on earth would make me fall off—I had seen those long jaws and vicious teeth in the bottom of the boat. After a while, I began to enjoy the sensation of flying over the water. Then the boat slowed, the engine coughed and was still, the board lost its life, and I was in the water. It was those five minutes—or was it ten?—while I was waiting for the boat to be restarted and circle back for me (it seemed to have drifted miles away) which made me reluctant forever afterwards to venture into deep unknown seas. I was numbed by the icy water but I did not splash or kick for fear of attracting attention. I remained motionless, except for touch-

ing my legs from time to time—they might have been bitten
off, I thought, without my even feeling it.

Jay congratulated me on not falling; and I, safe and
with a warm pullover round me, smiled and said it had
been great fun.

At that time the road through La Playa was the West
Coast's escape route from Prohibition; it was the highway
into Mexico. Anyone could cross the border for a day, and
almost everyone did. The traffic was heavy and all sorts
of accommodations had sprung up by the roadside—everything from hot-dog stands and restaurants to roadhouses
and nightclubs.

Jay had heard about the chef there, the floor show somewhere else, and he was curious. So I became acquainted
with the idiot world of Prohibition drinking: the crazy behavior, the stumbling walk, women in evening dress out
cold and carried off on stretchers. No one lifted an eyebrow;
the Hamiltons did not even look up. I was learning not to
be surprised at anything.

And I was learning to expect everything. Jay was offering
larger worlds, worlds where everything was possible. What
would I like to do? Anything in the world. Should we go
to his château on the Loire? We might watch a revolution
in Central America. What he suggested depended upon his
mood.

As well as his enthusiasms, Jay liked to share his feeling
of power. (And power he had, through money, high finance,
the web of finance.) Jay was a warm friend and he possessed the gift of friendship; I felt it—the knack of making
me feel that all I need do was to ask, and the world was

mine. Of course I never did ask, but the feeling was there, a fine new feeling which stayed and spread its roots like couch grass.

While I was eating breakfast or when I had come in to change for dinner, my grandmother sometimes stopped me for a few words. She did not question me about where I was going or what I was doing; it was as though the details did not matter. Her remarks were not beside the point and they were generally in the form of warnings: above all, I should not lose my head or my sense of reality. Life with the Hamiltons was quite different from everyday life. Of course I thought I knew that, or thought I knew better. I believe I thought that their kind of life was my kind—if I were clever. Jay had made it sound so simple, how he had turned himself from a rich man into a colossus. I would start with my gasoline discovery; if that didn't do the trick, there were hundreds of other things. I had only to think them up.

I had shown Jay my gasoline formula and he had taken it seriously. He had sent it off to his expert. If it was commercially sound, he would back it; that is, he would see that it was backed. A group of his friends often promoted that sort of thing, and he mentioned some well-known products.

In this talk with Jay, he very soon dismissed the subject of my formula and began telling me about one of his own. It had fallen into his hands in a business deal—a very simple formula; simple things were best. He'd hand it on to me if I liked. The trouble was it couldn't be patented; it was too simple for that. I would have to think up a good selling name and make it a household word by advertising.

He could help me with that but only up to fifty thousand. That would not be enough for a national campaign. I'd have to be sure of a half-million at least. If the gasoline worked, I'd have it.

The holidays ended on that hope. The Hamiltons went back to Pasadena and I to school, wiser in the knowledge that fifty thousand wasn't money.

VI

THE GASOLINE was out. The snag was the cost of production. Jay Hamilton wrote that there was nothing wrong with my process, but the manufactured gasoline would come to a few cents more a gallon than natural gasoline. He advised me to hold on to the formula because, at some moment, natural gas might run short. Or, if I wanted to produce gasoline in Europe, the market there was in my favor.

This news was a blow, but the full force did not strike at once as the letter came at the time of the big basketball game of the year. I was playing in that and I had the end-of-the-year exams on my mind. The disappointment came later. The flavor of it, I remember, had a great deal to do with the realization that if Jay had really been interested in my fortunes, he could have persuaded his friends to set up a plant in Europe. To him, it would have meant dictating a few letters. It wasn't as though they were going to lose money. But of course any investment was making money hand over fist in America at that time. Why should they bother?

I would have to think up something else.

The days of reckoning had come and gone: examinations, speech day, prizes, and finally report cards. I had an A average, which surprised me more than it did my grandmother. She took it as a natural part of my inheritance. I won three five-dollar-gold-piece prizes, which, when held in my hand, went a long way toward comforting me for the loss of a gasoline fortune.

That summer I did a great many different things in different places. I went on a motoring trip with the Randalls through the back country and into the desert. I stayed in Pasadena with the Hamiltons. At the end of the summer I was with Augusta and Andrew, who had finally moved to Laguna.

These were leisurely days of sun and sea and shade and being together. Often we would go off in the car for a picnic. After bathing, Augusta would unwrap the beautiful lunch, and while we sipped coffee hot from the thermos, Andrew read aloud or we talked. I sat with my back against a tree trunk looking out to sea, or I lay flat, my head on a folded pullover, staring up through the pine needles into the intense blue of the sky.

I loved most being with Augusta and Andrew. It was

peaceful to be with people who were so self-contained and happy together. I wondered at the disparity of outlook between the Randalls, the Hamiltons, Augusta and Andrew. Once inside, and a part of each family, one could feel how much each considered his way of living—his habits and standards—the most rational in the world. Each was certain of superiority. Like a chameleon, I slipped from one to the other, taking on the tone, the point of view, the idiom; and without a backward glance, I accepted each new set of values.

Andrew made me sit up and think. He teased me for trying to make my fortune as an alchemist. He teased me for admiring Jay Hamilton. What had he done for himself except manipulate money—a poker player on a monstrous scale? Then Andrew told me how he had renounced making money at the age of twenty-five. He had been sent from college straight out to Japan. He was on a mission to arrange for the installation of a telephone system for the whole island. He loved the life there and his work was agreeable. One evening, as he walked in the garden of the inn, it came over him that he had enough money to live without working, and that he owed it to himself to throw up his job. It was a hard decision for a young American man. It was against everything he had been brought up to believe. He would forfeit the respect of his compatriots; he would be without framework or prop; he would be thrown on his own resources. It was a challenge.

He had made the decision and never regretted it. On that lovely distant island he had had the peace in which to think. He had had a glimpse of what life could be like. Thank heavens, he had enough sense to see that the accumulation of money made little difference; it was only the lack of it that was ever felt.

At this, both Augusta and I breathed out an audible *Ahh*. Andrew glanced at us, and I asked where one could draw the line between the accumulation of money and the assurance of not lacking it.

We all laughed, and Andrew said that I should take his word for it: nothing was easier than making money.

I said I would like to, but how could he vouch for something that he had never tried?

"Fair enough," Andrew said, leaning forward. "Let's take an example. Look at the world. What is the popular rage at this moment?"

"Sitting on flagpoles."

"Marathon dancing."

"Sunbathing," Andrew said. "Getting a tan. It takes time and leisure. It's expensive. Thousands and hundreds of thousands of office girls will want to look like their more fortunate sisters. Think up a cheap bottled suntan, and you've got it."

"Easier said than done."

With a show of mock surprise, Andrew asked if I had not read Kipling, the Indian spy stories. The English secret agent rubs himself with a solution of potassium permanganate. It browns the skin; in fact, it oxidizes it—which is, in substance, what the sun does. Andrew tilted his hat farther over his nose. It was a gesture both of dismissal and of triumph.

Before I went back to school, he talked to me about it. If I was really interested, he said, he foresaw definite problems. Women do not like a watery makeup. I would have to make an oily solution. In contact with most oils, permanganate loses its force and turns brown. I might try glycerine; it would give me something to think about at school. In encouraging me like this, he was acting against his highest beliefs; if he had his way, girls would occupy themselves with the art of being attractive.

"You want us brought up like geishas?" I said, and saw that I had come almost too near the bone.

"It is an idea," he said coolly. "Have you ever known a man who liked a woman for her mind?"

I admitted I hadn't known one, but I had read of it.

"You see, it's pure fiction." He gave me a teasing look. "What's more, I'll wager your book was written by a woman."

Before I had embarked on it, I had expected to enjoy the senior year: to be an overlord, to have the other girls look up to you and respect you. *To be at the top.*

But how different the feeling, once there! It was cold and draughty as though the wall had gone from the precipice. There was nothing to lean against. The responsibility lay with us. (How I missed that class above me, the leaders and the models.) Now *we* had to set the tone, behave in an exemplary way, prod and cajole the younger girls. After class hours, there were meetings, decisions about policy, about deportment—the privileges and taboos. There were elections to offices for the school, for the class, for sports, for the school magazine.

Sonia and Mary and I sat at the back of these gatherings; as day girls, we were outside school machinery. But Mary and I were caught in another way; she was elected editor of the school magazine and I was made captain of the

Whites. Every girl at school was either a Blue or a White by the drawing of lots. It was a way of dividing the school for competitive games. As captain of the Whites, I would have to occupy myself with the various teams and with athletics in general. Miss Cunningham told me that my most important function was to bolster up the morale of the Whites. They had not won the school cup within the longest memory.

Sonia got off scot-free. Walking home afterwards, she said that she had been terrified that her abilities might have been acknowledged. What a blessing that our class was made up of grubs.

If school hours were packed, the evenings were no less taken up. Apart from the usual engagements, the theater in San Diego was extraordinary that year. The Barrymores came and Katharine Cornell, Cornelia Otis Skinner, Ruth Draper and others whose names I have forgotten. My grandmother took Sonia and me. It was far more important for us to see John Barrymore in *Hamlet*, she said, than to stay at home and stuff our heads like telephone directories.

Sometimes we met Augusta and Andrew there, and Grandmother would be put out that they hadn't let her know. They could have had dinner with us; at least, they might have stopped. Andrew said that Augusta was becoming like other women; she made up her mind at the last minute. Augusta said to me that she didn't know what it was; she felt too impatient to sit down to family talk—too impatient and restless. I suspected that my grandmother's ban on smoking—such a molehill in itself—made a mountain of difference to Augusta. I thought how strange that Grandmother should be such a Puritan toward herself and her family when to outsiders she was the soul of tolerance and, by some, considered revolutionary.

In the spring when the school term turned the corner from just-plodding-along into the straight, with the finishing post in view, and because for us, the seniors, it was now or never, we put our heads down and worked flat-out.

The chauffeur took over the driving at night, and when Grandmother came back very late, she would sometimes look in on me at my desk and say I shouldn't stay up so late, but she didn't interfere or bother me with talk.

One evening when I was immersed in physics, she came in and stood there without speaking at once. Naturally I had put my work down. "Augusta has not been feeling really well for some time," she said. Andrew had finally spoken to her about it. Of course Augusta was stubborn and courageous; she insisted that all she needed was to rest. But Andrew had spoken of her lack of spirit and sudden tears, and now Grandmother was disturbed by her color and loss of weight. So, between them, they had persuaded Augusta to go into the nursing home—the one across the street from my school—for a rest. It had been difficult to make her agree, but Andrew had pointed out that it was *the* place to rest; she'd be forced to.

Andrew had taken her there this afternoon. She had a pretty, cheerful room, and even seemed happy to be in bed. I shouldn't worry about it, Grandmother said. It was quite probable that Augusta was tired; she never spared herself. At the door she turned and nodded me back to work; she thought I ought to know, that was all, and Augusta had

given her the message that I should come in and see her
whenever I had a moment.

I cut study hour the next afternoon and rushed across the
street. I was reassured as soon as I saw Augusta. Her presence was always reassuring; how could it not be? She never
indulged herself in gloom (I remembered she had called it
self-indulgence when she spoke of our Wisconsin cousins'
gloom). I tried to read beneath her smile, but she looked
as she had always looked—if I discounted that her face had
not been made up and her hair, which was long and heavy,
was not in the usual low chignon but in two plaits to be
comfortable against the pillows.

When I asked how she felt, she laughed and said it was
Andrew's madness to bring her to such a formidable place
as this to spend a few days in bed. She asked me about
school. She was slightly sardonic about my being a captain
"of all those hockey girls." I had been explaining why the
honor of being White captain pressed so heavily now: the
big games were in the offing, with a thousand details to be
seen to. I had to be on the playing field after hours instead
of here with her.

I managed to see Augusta several times a week by cutting
afternoon study. She seemed to count on my coming, and
my school anecdotes seemed to amuse her. She remembered
them all and wanted to know what happened next. I found
I was exaggerating or inventing things to make her laugh.

What worried me was that Augusta did not seem to be
getting any better. She was not a person to stay in bed if
she had the energy to get up. One week, two weeks, three
weeks passed. And I could see—because I was allowed to
go to her room unannounced—that she no longer bothered

to read. Even the books which used to lie on her bed table had been moved.

I knew that Andrew and Grandmother were worried. The doctor had examined Augusta and could not find what was wrong. Grandmother said he was keeping her under observation, but nothing came of it. Andrew went to the nursing home in the mornings and sometimes drove all the way from Laguna again to have dinner with Grandmother. The mere act of driving, he said, was a help. Once in a while I dined with them but more often not. I made myself something quick and went to my room to study. It was to me what driving was to Andrew; anyway, I had to.

Two days before the final examinations, Miss Cunningham gave a talk to the seniors: advice, she said, which she had to give every year. We were all of us looking haggard. We must let up now and get some sleep. It was a grave mistake to face an ordeal in a state of nervous exhaustion.

I went to bed at eleven that night and fell into a heavy sleep. I was awakened by a ringing, the reason for which I did not gather until I heard my grandmother speaking into the telephone.

She came at once to my room. It was Andrew from the nursing home. Augusta had gone into a coma, and the doctor was not certain that she would last the night.

I jumped out of bed and started to dress, and it felt as though I were still held in a heavy dream. Grandmother was standing in my room with her hat and coat on, and we went out together to the garage. I do not think she spoke on the way to the nursing home. It was simply the telephone message which kept resounding back on my ears.

I followed Grandmother down the long corridor—which

smelled as always of ether—and into the room. There was a raucous whirring sound. The ceiling light was far too bright in that whiteness. Andrew was standing on the far side of the bed. He looked up as we came in; his face was wooden and did not change as he saw us.

Augusta might have been a plaster effigy. Only the modeling of the brow and the fine nose were familiar. Her mouth was open and the tearing rattle came from it.

After a while, I touched Grandmother on the arm and pointed to the chair. She sat down. Andrew walked out of the room and was gone for some time.

Back once more, he stood as before. I do not know how long we were like this. A gray-haired man in a dark suit came in with a nurse. Andrew started for the door, stopped and helped Grandmother from the chair, and we filed out.

Andrew led us to a small waiting room. He said he had asked the doctor to look at her again. He walked away from us and stood facing the black window. Grandmother sat motionless. I stood where I was and then I sat down.

When the doctor came in, Andrew turned to him. The doctor spoke in a normal speaking voice. He said it was a question of time. It might go on for an hour, two hours, twenty-four. Difficult to tell. It was unlikely that she would regain consciousness.

Andrew looked at his watch and then at Grandmother. He said it was two o'clock; she should do exactly as she pleased, but he advised her to go home and get some rest.

"Rest?" Grandmother said. Then she nodded. We both knew that Andrew wanted to be left to himself.

*   *   *

The sun woke me up and I gazed at Soledad with a blank mind. Slowly I took in that it was late. The silence in the house brought back to me the whole of last night. I slipped into the bathroom and ran a bath; then I could not bear not knowing and went in my dressing gown to look for Grandmother.

"She did not regain consciousness," she said. "She died at four o'clock." Grandmother turned and looked at me. "You are not dressed. You should be at school. Nothing is served by staying here."

On the way to school I remembered that the bath was still in the tub. The girls were crossing the quadrangle between classes when I got there, so I followed them and didn't have to explain my lateness. Miss Cunningham waylaid me at lunchtime and asked why I had not been at roll call. I told her and she seemed distressed for me. Did I want to go home now? But I knew that that would be worse. The examination tomorrow, she said, and put her hand on my shoulder, I should not worry about it; it did not really matter how I did. I would get by on my past record.

Miss Cunningham did not know how little it did matter. I had lost my reason for caring.

The rest of the school term was a succession of days, of sitting down to examination papers, of having to be there, of writing down answers. Andrew was often at the house with Grandmother, and when I came into the room, they not infrequently stopped what they were saying and went on with something else. I gathered that the doctor had performed an autopsy but I didn't hear with what result. Andrew and Grandmother were so on edge and brittle that I didn't find the heart to ask. For me, at least, nothing whatever could help or alter what had happened.

Graduation Day burst over us like a fireworks display; glory, laudation, and gold pieces flashed from the raised platform and fell in benediction, and below in the quadrangle were row upon row of parents and relations, the old girls come back, guests of honor and the pupils. Miss Cunningham described the senior class as standing on the brink of life, and we, at least, took her words to heart. The younger girls wriggled; they were beside themselves at the nearness of the holidays to come.

I was surprised to see that my grandmother was there. She had never come to other school functions. Then it struck me again that of course this was an occasion. She was sitting with a woman I had not seen before, rather elderly, with wide gray eyes and a penetrating look. When I came up to them afterwards to offer refreshments, Grandmother introduced her as Dean Yost of Stanford. I supposed they had been plotting my future because I knew that Grandmother wanted me to go to a coeducational college, preferably Stanford. They went on with their talk and it was surprisingly about their own college days, and soon Miss Cunningham joined them; they had all three been to Vassar.

That night my grandmother dined at school with Dean Yost and Miss Cunningham. I was included, too, out of courtesy, but I sat at a small table with my own classmates. Whenever I caught a glimpse of my grandmother, she appeared animated and interested. It was the first time she had been out since Augusta's death, and although she held that we must go on with our normal lives, until now I had not seen that she had. The summer stretched ahead, a dreadful blank.

When I drove Grandmother home, I left her at the front door and drove on to the garage. I dawdled over fastening the doors and walked slowly up through the garden. Recently I had rather tried to avoid finding myself alone with my grandmother; it was so difficult to know what to say.

She was waiting for me in the patio and she had thrown off her own wall of silence. She said how pleasant Dean Yost was and Miss Cunningham, too, for that matter. I was afraid she might end abruptly but she went on. A proposition had been put to her. An invitation, rather— from the Jay Hamiltons. They were taking Camilla to Hawaii this summer and had asked if I might go, too.

Grandmother said I should make up my own mind. I knew what she thought of their way of living; it could easily distort a young person's sense of values.

Would I like to go?

Hawaii meant nothing to me except rather sickly ukulele music. But I could not resist the thought of getting away.

"It might be a good idea for you to get away just now," Grandmother said. "You did love her, did you not, very much?"

VII

CAMILLA AND I were pushed into the royal suite at the last minute. Our original cabin had been everything I could have asked for: the door opened straight on to the deck— the sea was there. Camilla and I stepped out to watch the coastline dwindle, and Jay came up and stood between us at the rail. He now wore a soft cap and the expression of a man who enjoys being at sea. As soon as we had cast off, he said, the purser offered him the royal suite. He wanted a sitting room, but he didn't want to saddle himself with a place where every Tom, Dick, and Harry would drop in for a drink. He had seen the passenger list and there were some people he would not be able to avoid. Then it came to him to put Camilla and me in the suite—no one would barge in on two girls. He could give a party *when* and *if* he liked. So he had asked that we be moved and his drink trunk put in the sitting room.

The suite might as well have been inside a hotel. It was enclosed and airless. The entrance was at the top of the great staircase. I decided to spend my time on deck. Camilla was not enthusiastic, either. But Jay paid no attention to us; he was examining the rooms. This ship had been taken over by America after the war, he said. He'd heard that it had been the Kaiser's private yacht: a fine ship, beautiful lines.

At the dock I had been disappointed in its size; it had looked small next to the loading shed. Now that I wandered through it, I found that I had misjudged it: there was lounge after lounge, a library, a playroom for children, a gymnasium, and a large cement swimming pool, not yet filled. As soon as the ship started to roll, Camilla went back to the cabin to lie down, and I went on exploring. I liked best the top deck where you could feel the wind and see forever. Here the wires and ropes hummed, and the sound matched the excitement in the pit of my stomach. I had two deck chairs brought—one for Camilla tomorrow—and there I stayed for the rest of the afternoon.

When I went down, the Hamiltons were in our sitting room and Camilla was up and in a chair. Jay was telling her that seasickness was nothing more than imagination. Imagination locked the muscles. Relax, he said; *to relax was the secret.* He gave the bottle in the ice bucket a turn. "You'll drink a glass of this—you, too," he said to me as though I were about to escape from a family doctoring. Camilla did look on the verge of flight.

I had never tasted champagne and I expected a great deal. It was like peculiar soda water. Camilla said it made her feel better and drank another glass. I felt exactly the same, but I took the next glass to give it every chance. We went down to dinner without changing; Jay said nobody bothered the first night out.

I was wide-awake early the next morning. Camilla was sleeping and I knew she would be far happier to stay like that. I looked in after breakfast and she was still asleep, so I went on up to the top deck and lay in the sun. I had left off my stockings on purpose and I was wearing a short tennis dress. When the front of me felt baked, I spread the steamer rug on a raised platform and lay face downward. I was completely alone with the sun and sea. Only once a woman came up looking for her son Roger. She was worried he would dive into the swimming pool before they put the water in. I asked how old he was, expecting her to say six or seven.

"Going on for fourteen but he doesn't notice things."

"He'd notice *that*," I said, but she had walked away still calling his name.

At lunchtime Camilla was propped up in bed on one elbow with her breakfast tray untouched beside her. I told her it was hopeless as long as she stayed shut up in the cabin. She ought to come up to the top deck with me. Her mother was in the doorway and agreed. We offered to help her, but Camilla shook her head. She'd try, after a while.

I told her about Roger because that was the sort of joke she liked. Mrs. Hamilton said how extraordinary it was: she had never yet been on a ship which didn't have a Roger and his mother and the swimming pool.

That evening Jay gave a cocktail party, which meant that our cabin door had to be kept shut. It was like being inside a chocolate box. I sat with Camilla, and her mother came in from time to time bringing champagne and trying to persuade Camilla to get up. After the third glass, she did. I helped her fasten the back of her dress. When we emerged, the others had already gone down to dinner.

The orchestra was in full swing at the foot of the stairs. To make an entrance down a wide staircase and to music needs a good deal of dignity. As we came to the last steps, the music broke off in mid-bar. The entire dining room looked up. I saw that something had made the orchestra helpless. I followed Camilla to the table. Jay and Mrs. Hamilton were laughing, too. My face and neck and forearms were scarlet—startling against white shoulders and the rest of my arms exposed by an evening dress. No wonder the orchestra couldn't blow into their horns.

After that night almost everybody I passed on the ship nodded or spoke to me. I was asked to take part in shuffle-board and deck tennis and in funny competitions like three-legged races and running with an egg in a spoon. I would make my escape to the top deck, which remained remarkably deserted.

Camilla had given up the struggle to be a good sailor. It was a hard defeat for her because of the way she felt about her father, and she was all too conscious of the fact that he could not bear weaklings. I stayed out of the way not to be a reminder of rude health. I saw—or imagined I did—whales spouting on the horizon. When I wasn't gazing out to sea, I read. Most of the books in the ship's library I already knew.

I was rereading Thornton Wilder's *The Cabala* when I looked up from the page to find a young god in modern dress sitting in the deck chair meant for Camilla.

"The sun acolyte," he said as though recognizing a cousin, and stretched out his hand for my book. He saw the library mark and asked if I had come without provisions. He had dozens to lend me, given him at the train in New York. People always give such cumbersome things to travelers. Not that a man was bothered with flowers, but the amount of books! He had had to buy an extra suitcase en route. I would like the one he had finished yesterday, *Futility*, by William Gerhardi. He would bring it after lunch.

This trip was a lark—it was the first time he and his two brothers had ever traveled alone together. He had just finished his first year at Yale, his older brother was in the class above him, and the younger one was going to Harvard in the autumn—to change the pattern.

He was the easiest person in the world to talk to, and as the morning passed I had a glimpse of the brothers. They appeared singly, and when they saw that their brother was with a girl, they went off again. Mine, the middle one, was by far the handsomest, but there was a strong likeness, the carved look.

In the afternoon he brought the book and said to pass it on to another needy soul when I had finished with it. He asked if he was taking someone else's chair, and I told him about Camilla. He said the effect of champagne lasted no longer than the bubbles. What she should do was to eat those floury baked potatoes ships always have. Plain without butter. If she didn't like potatoes, the next best thing was a diet of giant green olives.

That night when we were in bed I told Camilla all about everything and that he had said I should call him Freddy. She liked neither potatoes nor olives, Camilla said, but I had made her want to get up to see the paragon. Then she warned me to keep him out of Jay's way—she was speaking from experience. "He is against young men."

"But why?" I asked.

"He thinks we're still babies, you'll see." Camilla gave her sheet an exasperated jerk. "He tells *me* they're after my money."

"You don't believe him!"

It was a shock when she merely shook her head, "It could be true."

One couldn't argue with Camilla. I switched on my reading light and opened *Futility*. At once I was swept into a deliciously funny worldly world. How clever of Freddy to know it would strike the right note! When I told him so the next morning, he did not say—as I realized later he had every right to—that half the world had acclaimed it in the very words I had used. He said he knew I would like it by the way my mouth curled.

On my way to change for dinner I found Jay alone in the sitting room, the door to the cabin was shut. He said he had seen me on the top deck with that young man. We'd even had deck chairs brought.

I said that he had been in Camilla's chair.

I was under his care, Jay said, and he forbade me absolutely to see the fellow.

"But why?" I asked.

"Because I promised your grandmother to look after you."

"She doesn't mind my talking to young men."

73

"Will you do as I say?" Jay looked thunderous.

I knew that I must, and nodded.

The door of the cabin opened and a mountain of a man with snowy hair and a white walrus mustache came out. He was rubbing his hands with glee. Jay said that Dr. Bancroft was an old friend from Chicago. Dr. Bancroft said that Camilla would join us in a few moments; he was sure she would. He looked round as though he hoped for a larger stage. "I've dosed her with strychnine"—and now he gave me a mischievous look—"strong enough to kill a dog." Jay took a step toward the door but Dr. Bancroft stopped him. "Don't worry, my boy. She'll be as fit as a fiddle. I take it every morning at sea."

Camilla did join us. And from then on she stayed on her feet, which made my part much easier. I couldn't have gone to the top deck if I had wanted to; now that Camilla was with us, the Hamiltons did everything in a body. We all, including Dr. Bancroft, sat in a long row of deck chairs on the windless side of the shaded middle deck.

On the last morning I woke up with the feeling that something was different. The ship was smooth, quite as though it were slipping on silk. Curiosity made me throw on some clothes and go out on deck. Ahead, an island lay dark against a pearly sea. The sun was at that moment rising, and it touched the sky and water with pink. It was breathtaking: a serene enactment of the first Creation.

I had thought the deck deserted, but now at the prow I saw three still figures: Freddy and his brothers, looking ahead, their backs to me.

VIII

THE HOTEL was charming; not one of those white plaster palaces directly on Waikiki Beach. It was low, under co-conut palms, a dark wood main building and individual cottages very like my idea of Japanese houses; walls could be shifted or rolled back, leaving only the wire screen against the soft night. A mossy lawn ended in a palm-fringed prom-enade a few feet above the sea. To the left one looked out across the blinding sands of Waikiki to Diamond Head.

Camilla said how lovely to live in this cave of coolness. The shade was her haven and mine was the sun. I spent the mornings riding the surf, not on one of those famous boards so heavy that it needed a native man to push it through the mile of tumbling waves; but unencumbered,

I flung myself onto any breaker that caught my fancy. I baked myself on the sands until the tepid water was cool by contrast. A half hour before lunch Camilla would appear, protected by a straw hat and a short silk coolie coat. I would take a last gentle swim with her, groggy now with sun and salt, hungry, happy at the thought of the beaded ice water, the waiting dining room.

In the afternoons Camilla and I were driven up across the mountains to the golf course. The Hamiltons had brought their own car with them, a Cadillac with a specially built body. It was so low to the ground that it was useless except on a paved road. Jay, who had come to the island to paint and wanted to do it in out-of-the-way places, found he had to hire a taxi. So Camilla and I were left with the car and Hawkins.

On the way to the golf course was a high exposed pass, which had notices saying to hold on to the car hood to prevent it from being blown off. This pass was like going through the wind tunnel at a fun fair. Camilla and I waited for this moment with glee, all the more so because our hood was down. When we came to the sign, Hawkins took his cap off and looked at his inside mirror to see that we were well down and ready. We drove in slowly. What we all hoped for was to meet cars coming from the opposite direction, and sometimes we did: high rickety ones with brown arms stretched to the canvas, clinging on for dear life, hilarious grins inside.

Hawkins enjoyed it as much as we did. Camilla had known Hawkins all her life, and now I noticed that there was a bond between them, a curious one of jokes. It was a new side to Camilla. The background of their conversation was Marx Brothers quips (on the order of "I'd horsewhip you if I had a horse," although this one I discovered for myself later). She and Hawkins had a wonderful time comparing tidbits from the island newspapers. Camilla spotted the prize headline: CANNIBALS IN UGLY MOOD.

The golf course, too, had its own joke. At certain times of the day, without fail and to the minute, it poured with rain—a tropical rain like a tap being turned on and like a tap only over definite stretches. At these holes, under a giant umbrella, was the notice giving the exact time of the downpour and how long it would last, and there was a stand holding small umbrellas for anyone who wanted to walk the hundred yards to bright sunshine.

On the golf course I found still another Camilla: the fanatic golfer. She was tough, tireless, energetic, enthusiastic—a scratch player. She wore sturdy brogues and no hat. She did not notice the sun. She knew par for each hole, and if she did not keep to it, she was under.

At night we were invited to dine with one or another of the old established island families. Fabulous affairs, they seemed to me, made so by the magic of the setting: terraced on the mountainside, overlooking a luminous sea, with the moon hung in the plumed palms; music, dancing, the soft attentiveness of the native servant boys.

No one would ever have guessed, we all agreed, that these old families had been the missionaries of a hundred years ago. The wealth of the islands had been heaped onto the laps of the firstcomers; and in three generations they had become worldly, international, intermarried with the lords of every land.

We were elaborately fêted. We were shown every island

77

sight through glass-bottomed boats and from motor launches. In the darkness, we saw the natives fish with torch and spear; we were driven to see exotic blooms which opened once every hundred years and then only at night; we were led through opium dens in Honolulu—paper houses neat and new as a pin and disappointingly empty. We watched, brought together especially for us, a last handful of elderly natives who remembered the intricate old dances which were a formalized miming of ancient myth, no swish of grass skirts to show up a pretty figure, but the massive roll and thrust of nature. Nor did the music resemble the twanging of hotel orchestras; it was a tom-tom beat to cries which brought sweat out on the forehead.

We ate sun-ripened pineapples sweet from the fields and avocados in the hand with no more ado than a pinch of salt. We visited sugar plantations and refineries, and at once Jay proposed another way for me to make my fortune. I should start a factory for gingersnaps: make them almost entirely of molasses—molasses was being given away at a dollar a ton—make and package them on the island, where native labor was cheap, and ship them to the entire world. Again, it sounded simple, and this time I took it as it was meant to be, a pleasant daydream to a man like Jay, to anyone with the initial half-million.

We were taken for a week's cruise round the islands. At dawn on the second day we passed an island as lovely as paradise, which the captain unbelievably said was the leper colony. We made but one stop and that was on the island of Mauna Loa. The island had an active volcano and a famous German scientist with (at that time) the most sensitive seismographs in existence. The most accurate one, he told us, he had built himself and he had weighted it with his wife's flatiron. Three days ago she had missed her favorite iron, and now she wanted it back. She swore not to speak to him until she had it. It was a lonely place when there was no one to talk to. He was so glad we had come.

We were the only guests in a great barn of a hotel. Nearby, Camilla discovered a derelict golf course. From every crack and crevice, even from the holes of the greens, steam spurted. The beaches were of black volcanic sand. Mammoth ferns took the place of trees on the mountainside and grew in a thick impenetrable tangle. Camilla said the whole place made her feel that she was dead and had awakened in Hades. The sky was overcast and it rained a steady fine rain.

Jay hired a car and a guide to take us up to the crater. On the way, we stopped in the fern jungle and were shown the opening of a tunnel, high enough for a man to walk upright in, which the lava had burned in the flank of the volcano. It was one of many. The crater itself was like a gigantic cook pot, a mile deep and a mile wide. Steam came up from the liquid rock on the boil. Bubbles of what looked like a fluid mud-pie mixture rose and broke. It was fascinating to watch. I must have gone too near the edge. I felt the ground give way, and the next thing I knew I was being jerked backwards by my coattails. It was the guide who had grabbed me. Camilla and I laughed a little hysterically and Jay said how like me.

When the excitement had died down, I was left with a headache, which got worse. Camilla gave me her bottle of aspirins. The next day the pain seemed to have settled in my ear. We were back on the boat now. Camilla said I would go crackers if I went on taking so many aspirins. We were sharing a cabin, and sometimes I thought she looked at me as though she were shut up with a dangerous animal.

As soon as we docked in Honolulu, Jay took me to a doctor who examined my ear, conferred with Jay, and, without a word to me, administered an anesthetic. When I came to, I was taken to a hospital. I was so relieved to be out of pain that I could have skipped for joy. Going to a hospital now seemed stable-door nonsense. The doctor said that he had punctured my eardrum and had taken particles of sand from the inner ear. I must have got them there from swimming with my mouth open in the churned-up surf. He wanted me in the hospital because he was draining the inner ear and watching it for a mastoid condition.

Jay never did things by halves. He called in another specialist. A battle of opinions began: the first doctor maintained that the condition was critical; the new doctor that it was plain sailing, a mere matter of time. In the mornings the first doctor dressed my ear, and in the afternoons the other doctor took the dressings away. Camilla came to see me every day and brought books and flowers and news about what each doctor had said to Jay. Of course I was restless lying in bed when I felt perfectly all right. The sun was glorious on the balcony and I had glimpses of the sea.

One afternoon Camilla arrived with the news that the first doctor was going to operate for mastoid. It was a serious operation, Camilla said, because it was so near the brain. And they would all have to stay on for at least another month. I wouldn't be back in time to start college.

Camilla stayed with me until the afternoon doctor came.

When we asked how my ear was, he said, "Fine!" It would have healed by now if it had been given the chance. (He never directly referred to the other doctor or the dressings.)

I asked if he could get me removed—or released—from the hospital. *He* couldn't, he said, because he had not brought me here. But it was a free country, he'd heard. He turned to Camilla, "I'm going now," he said, "by a convenient side entrance."

They went out together. I was dressed and packed by the time she came back. The corridor was clear. Camilla led the way past two doors and then she pushed open a frosted glass one. It was the side stairway. Hawkins had the car at the door with the engine running.

Jay was delighted that we had taken matters into our own hands. The medical deadlock was broken, our reservations for sailing could stand, and he would not have to cable my grandmother that I was having a serious operation. That evening he opened a bottle of Château Yquem 1911 and told Camilla and me to drink ours slowly, we were not apt to taste the like again.

The next morning I woke up stone-deaf. The afternoon doctor was summoned. He wrote down on a pad for me that it was nothing, it would pass, I must have patience. I did not hear a sound when people spoke; I could not have heard a cannon if it had gone off. The absolute silence made me feel that I was shut up under a glass diving bell. Even in this isolation it did not occur to me to distrust the doctor I wanted to believe.

My days were not unhappy. I learned very quickly to lip-read; at least, simple daily things. The Hamiltons went out a great deal. The Crown Prince of Sweden had come

81

to Honolulu and the whole island was fêting him. Camilla scrawled it all off on paper when she got home. Half the time she put at the end that she envied me, staying at home. She was fed up because as soon as a young man was agreeable and attentive, her father broke it up. I told her she would have to become a nun, and she wrote back that her father distrusted Catholicism as much as young men.

The doctor had forbidden me to go into the rough surf, so I swam in front of the hotel where the water was deep and quiet. There was no sand beach, but I lay on the raft and was rocked by the sea. I spent the best part of the day there, thinking, dipping in and out.

It was curious not to hear a sound from the outside world; it was rather as though I had been turned inward into my own mind. I no longer fought against thinking of Augusta. As the days passed, I began to accept what had happened. I faced my loss. I faced the fact that there was no one left who accepted me as myself, whole. No one who would accept me with my faults. No one I could discuss problems with. Grandmother, I knew, was interested only in qualities.

Three days before we were to sail for home, I was awakened by a knock on the door. I said, "Come in," and the boy wheeled in the breakfast trays. It was all so natural that I did not take it in until I saw Camilla's expression. "Thank goodness," she said, "we've been worried to death."

On board ship Dr. Bancroft did not give Camilla a chance to succumb. They both took strychnine pills every morning and were as lively as crickets. The summer seemed to have done Dr. Bancroft a world of good. He spent the whole day on deck, walking miles with any of us who could be persuaded. On the rounds with him I spoke about Augusta's death. I found it possible because he was a doctor and had never known her. He said it might have been leukemia which had not been recognized or diagnosed in time. Putting a name to it did not help much—nothing would—but it anchored it. It was known, closed, finished.

At the Los Angeles docks, the customs men insisted upon opening everybody's luggage. I was in a different queue from the Hamiltons but we were near enough to talk. I was almost light-headedly carefree because the night before I had thrown overboard my secret contraband. I had got hold of it with difficulty, I had concealed it with difficulty, and at last I had managed to get rid of it. I had had to slip up to the cabin while Camilla was dancing to take it out from under my clothes. It was a bottle of *okolehao*, the native drink, a fiery distillation of the islands. I had heard that half a glass was enough to send a strong man crazy. I was curious to taste it, so I had asked Hawkins to buy me a bottle. I did not realize that I had put him in a difficult position or that I was doing anything seriously wrong until Hawkins slipped a note into my hand (that was when I was deaf) on the outside of which he had written, "Please destroy this." The inside said that the bottle was concealed under my bed. I put it between my pullovers and forgot it. When I was packing, I found it and took it with me on board ship. I forgot it again until the last night, the night of the fancy-dress ball. In the middle of the dance, I went up to throw the bottle away. It seemed such a pity to waste all Hawkins's and my worry that I poured out half a glass and drank it. It seemed to evaporate in my mouth. The taste was not pleasant, there was no effect: it could have been anything.

Standing now in the queue, happy that I had got rid of the bottle, I felt more guiltless than even an innocent person has a right to.

The customs man rummaged through my clothes and pounced on a string of carved beads. "They're a kind of nut," he said and he began shouting about blight and pests. Jay Hamilton was at my side and the man turned to him. It came out that nothing was worse than being caught with a fragment of agriculture, no matter how ancient or tricked up.

IX

My GRANDMOTHER was satisfied with her arrangements. She had decided to send me to Stanford. My father's closest friend—apart from Jay Hamilton—had been a cousin of Jay's, Roderick Montgomery. Roderick Montgomery had died some years ago and now his widow lived in Palo Alto, the town where Stanford was. It so happened that Mrs. Montgomery's daughter Elizabeth was starting in at Stanford the very year I was. What could be more fitting than for us to be roommates?

I was sent off to Palo Alto a few days ahead of time to make the acquaintance of the Montgomery family: Elizabeth and the two younger boys. I was more struck with Mrs. Montgomery. She must have been an arresting beauty; now she was left with a distinguished face. She had handed on to her children a look of character but without the pleasing symmetry of her own features. The house, too, had its particular atmosphere. From the moment of stepping into the hall with the casual disorder of rackets, bats, and roller skates, you knew you were in a stronghold of children. Elizabeth's brothers were being sent off to school, so the house was in an uproar of packing and farewell parties. Hordes of little boys from the ages of twelve to sixteen came, and Elizabeth had asked four of her old school friends who were going to Stanford. It seemed to be taken for granted that we should all play charades together. One of the rooms off the drawing room was chockablock with dressing-up silks and brocades and plumed hats; the room was even called the charade room. It was a childish romp, and halfway through the evening we all had ice cream and cake and lemonade.

The next day Mrs. Montgomery had a private talk with me. She hoped I would consider her as taking the place of my grandmother. She would always be there to give advice and help. Elizabeth brought all her problems to her; they discussed *everything*. Then she told me I should feel free to use the tower room at the top of the house—it was the children's sanctum.

It was a large square room with windows on all four sides. Roderick, the older boy, who was to come to Stanford the next year, was up there. He was sitting on the floor, rolling a cigarette with great care. He asked if I would like one, and rolled a second. I thought that at last we were wiping the milk from our chins. My cigarette tasted odd and I asked what it was. "Tea leaves," he said. "Mother allows us to smoke anything as long as it isn't tobacco."

Mrs. Montgomery came with Elizabeth and me to the Freshman Hall to see that we were comfortably installed. I was rather relieved to find that being a roommate did not mean sharing a room. There were two bedrooms, one on either side of a communal study, and a bathroom. Mrs. Montgomery went home to fetch an extra standing lamp and some vases for flowers.

Before I had finished unpacking, shouts and giggles came from the study. It was Elizabeth and her four school friends. They all called her "Monty," and Monty was evidently the leader; our study became the headquarters where they all studied. They were inseparable, the five of them; they took the same classes, ate at the same table in the dining room, went about the campus as a fivesome, thought the same thoughts and communicated them in their particular school language.

At the beginning, Hall was divided into these knots of friends who had come up from the same school. They stuck to each other by habit. I drifted into friendship with a few solitary ones who seemed to be older than the rest of us. Of course I did not ask why they were still in Hall, because even I knew that at the end of the first year the popular girls were chosen by sororities and went to live on that great shaded avenue of the elect.

Monty enlightened me but only after it was too late to withdraw—by that time I had really become friends with them. Monty said I had deliberately sought out sorority observers and girls who held office on the council of the student body. She accused me of "sucking up." Most of the things I did irritated Monty. We had started off on the wrong foot. If it hadn't been for me, she could have been happily rooming with one of her own friends. I was thoroughly awkward because I didn't even fit myself into their gang. I had never been able to concentrate in a group with remarks and giggles going on; so I left them to study in our room and went out to the library.

Monty got it into her head that I had dates all the time even though I went out with books under my arm. It was only when the first examination papers came out and she heard my marks were higher than hers that I realized how angry she was about that, too. We had gone to a tea party which our French professor was giving for his students. When he came up to me and congratulated me on my paper, Monty broke into the conversation like a hornet. In front of everybody, she said I could only have done it by cheating—I never studied; she knew. There was silence. The professor, who had looked perplexed (he was going over the matter in his mind and I suppose he realized that nothing short of knowing in advance what the questions were would have helped), smiled again at me. "Miss Montgomery says you are not a drudge. It is a high compliment." And with that, he moved on. Monty did not try to interfere between me and my professors again.

Another thing which rankled in Monty's life was the fact that her mother (her own mother who was so close to her) should treat me to lunch sometimes in Palo Alto. I admired Mrs. Montgomery's style and appearance, and she could be amusing when she forgot to pump me for confidences. Being used to her daughter's flood of talk, she probably found me secretive, and she was a woman to suspect reticence. I believe it was my being such a *dark* horse that tipped the scales against me in the end. Monty tattled what she could. I know she told her mother that I smoked tobacco. Mrs. Montgomery said she'd heard, and did I? She asked if my grandmother knew, and I said that I would not dream of causing her unnecessary worry by telling her. Mrs. Montgomery said she believed in frankness.

It was through my own doing that my friendly relationship with Mrs. Montgomery was brought to a close. It was a thoughtless silly thing. A friend of mine from Miss Cunningham's was now going to boarding school in Palo Alto. I told Mrs. Montgomery that I would like to see her, and she said nothing could be easier. She was known to the women who ran the school, and if she asked them, she was certain they would allow my friend to have lunch with us. And so it was arranged. After lunch, Mrs. Montgomery asked how we were going to spend the afternoon, and when we said, "At the moving pictures," she left us. It was a fine autumn day and someone had lent me a car, so we went for a drive instead. We had started off in the direction of San Francisco, and as we were passing a small private airfield, we were both caught by an advertisement for short trial flights, a bargain offer: four-fifty for one person, five dollars for two. We went up. Nothing more than that, and then I drove her back to school.

A few days later—early in the morning before I was out of bed—Mrs. Montgomery burst in on me. I had betrayed her confidence. I had endangered a girl's life. I had ruined the school's confidence in her, Mrs. Montgomery. I had put an end to her confidence in me.

89

I protested.

Mrs. Montgomery marched out with the parting shot that I must report at once to Dean Yost; she had sent for me.

Dean Yost was not unfriendly—a lion would not have seemed unfriendly after the interview I had been through —she began by saying that the head of the boarding school had asked her to speak to me. I had committed a thoughtless act. She hoped I would not take any more school girls up in the air. Then she asked how my grandmother was and said that she had been pleased with my professors' accounts of my work.

I took Dean Yost's tact at its face value and understood that she had dismissed the incident. What I did not realize then was that whatever one did, one's every action, fell into a place in the making up of a reputation.

I was sorry that Mrs. Montgomery had been so completely upset. Our friendliness never revived. Now I was on my own at the university.

I went to some general meetings of the women students. The various students who spoke referred to us—the women —as *the cream*. "We must remember that we are the cream," they said. "We have greater responsibilities because we are the cream." It seemed strange that one should call oneself that. Granted that Stanford was a man's college (there were five men to each woman) and it was difficult for a woman to get in—about sixty a year were accepted, only the top layer: presumably *that* was the skimming which made us the cream—nonetheless, it did seem a presumptuous blowing of one's own horn. I looked round at us and saw that it was really a singing in the dark. Taken all together, we were an unattractive lot of bespectacled bluestockings. Most Stanford men ignored our existence; they went to the far pastures—to Berkeley—when they wanted to date girls.

Stanford stood high in football fame. Red Grange was the hero of the day and it was the fashion for the men to look tough. Shaving was scorned until late in the day. Dirty string-colored corduroys with an old pullover were the accepted campus gear (blue jeans for first-year men). What with their prejudice against Stanford women and their unkempt appearance, I was put off making friends with the men at first. In time I collected a few: a blond football giant called "Dainty" as an escort to dances; Eddy Cavendish, who was romantic-looking and played the piano; but my true standby was a rather intelligent ugly man. Hal Forbes was ugly in an unredeeming sharp-faced fox-terrier sort of way; that is, if a fox terrier could be imagined with pomade on his hair. He was an editor of the college newspaper. He had a rattletrap of a car and a passionate knowledge and love of San Francisco. This last brought us together and kept us friends.

He was in one of my classes, and one day when we were walking back to the quadrangle together, I said that I had never been to San Francisco. He was transfixed; he offered to drive me there next Saturday morning. We'd have a seafood lunch at the stalls along the waterfront, drive up on the hills to look at the Golden Gate, and wander through Chinatown in the late afternoon. That had been in the middle of the week, and by the end of it, I was doubtful if he would remember.

Hal came before ten, shaved, in a suit, and alive with enthusiasm. It was a sunny winter morning, and he decided that the bird's-eye view must come first. He was a prince showing the wonders of his capital. Every response whipped his fervor. I do not know whether the city danced in our eyes or we danced in its. The seafood tasted as though it had just been scooped out of the water. We sat in an out-door booth, soaking up sun and the clamor of the port. I was shown Market Street, cable cars, side streets, hilltops; we drove through the Chinese quarter and then we walked back through it, looking in shops, down alleyways, everywhere.

Over a counter open to the street, Hal bought a sack of dried melon seeds. To eat them properly, he said, we'd have to go into the Chinese theater. On the stage was a *tableau vivant* of the paintings we had seen in the shops. Splendid robes with long hanging sleeves and above them devil faces or empty haughty ones. "Masks," Hal said, and showed me how to eat the melon seeds. The theater was three-quarters full of Chinese men, all nibbling. The audience was in a state of constant flux. A group of men would stand up and walk out, a few more took their places. I tried to follow what was happening on the stage, but Hal said not to bother too much. He had never seen the beginning or the end of a play; it went on and on perhaps for weeks. It seemed to me that the masks were symbolic and I tried to sort them out into Evil, Power, Innocence, and Poverty, but I have no reason to think I was right. The only time I was startled was when one of the actors folded back his sleeve and revealed a naked hand.

When we went out, the streetlights were lit; it was night. Hal said we ought to have something to eat. We drove to another part of town to a small steamy Italian restaurant where Hal was greeted like a lost brother. The tables downstairs were crowded and so we were led upstairs to a private room. The waiter brought in a fiasco of Chianti and a great bowl of tagliatelle with lumps of butter and parmesan. When we were sitting over coffee, I suddenly remembered that I hadn't signed in the book for a late night. We left in a hurry and raced back. Hal managed to get me to the Hall in the nick of time, just as the door was about to be locked.

If San Francisco was not an obsession, it was a near obsession. On Saturdays Hal and I went as often as we could both make it. The first day had formed the pattern, although later on we generally started after lunch and stayed longer; I signed to be late.

Hal knew any number of Italian restaurants, most of which flourished as speakeasies on the side. It was in one of these that Hal, by not losing his head, won my respect and gratitude. Again we were upstairs; we heard below a sudden scraping of chairs and voices. Without a second's hesitation, Hal handed me my coat and pushed me out and down a back stairway, through a cellar tunnel into an alley, and with a sharp turn, back again into a bright busy street. "A police raid," he said. I trembled to think what might have happened if he hadn't been so quick, or if we had been in a place without a secret exit. "They've all got one," he said. "They have to."

Spring unsettled us all. It was hard to keep our noses stuck in our books. Sometimes in the afternoon, Hal would drive me to the small lake behind the Hall and we would wander along the edge under the trees. He was moody and preoccupied, and at last he told me the reason. During the Christmas holidays—it was on his twenty-first birthday—his mother had pulled his whole world down round his head. She had told him that he had been adopted as a baby. She broke down under his pleadings and swore she knew nothing about his parents—it was a rule of the adoption home. He vowed that he would find out. This was tricky, twenty years later. He got nowhere. And that was admitting a lot for him. He believed he could ferret out anything; it was his job. He had worked as a reporter for years during the summer months—a star at it, too.

"Do you think I come from idiot parents?"

We both laughed at the absurdity.

He went on and on: *he had to know who he was*. I told him to try to forget it. He was himself. He was the same as before Christmas.

He would never be the same, he said.

Eddy Cavendish had a canoe, and we went on the lake after dinner. We drifted on the black water while he endlessly quoted Walt Whitman, whom he had just discovered. I leaned against the cushions and watched the stars. When he ran out of verse, he improvised on the earth, the grass, spring, fertility. Did I realize my great good fortune in being a woman? to be able to create merely by being oneself? "If I were one," he said, "I would feel myself *the universe*."

I let him go on talking. The trouble with him was that he was planning to write a world-shattering symphony and he couldn't get down to it.

* * *

Dainty was an entirely gay companion; spring only increased his intoxication with college life—he was able to make of it a satisfactory reflection of his own daydreams. Scruffy as the scruffiest all day long, at night he became the peacock. Arrayed in a tuxedo or even in tails, he would call for me in somebody's shining limousine. He would drive me to the St. Francis Hotel in San Francisco or to a dance in the enemy's camp, at Berkeley.

It was through Dainty (and his insistence on doing what's done) that I ran into curfew trouble; it was *not* the fashion for a man to hobble himself with a girl's lockout rules. Once, twice, I got away with it; the third time I was locked out. I was called up before a committee of the student body. It was the supreme authority; we students were self-governing. At the outset of the hearing I was warned that the penalty could be expulsion. What had I to say for myself?

I was thunderstruck that one could be expelled, not for wrongdoing, but for the half hour here or there. Words came, reasons; I had a good deal to say for myself and I said it with the conviction of innocence. (How different if it had happened after being with Hal at a speakeasy!) I was succeeding, I was talking my way out, I saw sympathy awakening in the faces of my judges.

There was a short wait before the verdict. Then it was pronounced: considering it was my first offense, considering my scholastic record, considering everything, if from now on I took care, if I kept my slate clean, nothing further would be said.

As the spring term drew to an end, the great hullabaloo started: sorority rushing. It was brought home to us in Hall that we had been under scrutiny from the beginning. Those who had found favor were sent invitations to various sororities; those who had not, not. We went in trembling chattering groups to be inspected at close range. Our destinies were about to be sealed here and now. We were about to be placed in the world. It would mean everything for the next three years: social position, friends, chances.

The girls who got no invitations were already face to face with their fate, and they were wretched. We all said it was a shame and undemocratic. Some of us talked about a revolt. If the entire class refused to play, it would be a blow to the system. But the majority of girls with invitations could not be moved. Although they perfectly well knew that an invitation to tea did not mean that they would be bid for, they couldn't help hoping—the chase was on and blood was up.

I was less concerned than most, because the question of sororities had no place in my outside world: I could imagine my grandmother's indifference and the Hamiltons', and how Sonia would smile. But a lot of the girls had mothers who belonged to sororities and wanted their daughters to be in the same ones. Other mothers hoped that their daughters would do better than they had. Poor Monty was in a cleft stick. Mrs. Montgomery wanted her to join her own sorority, which had a high national standing but which happened not to be a top one at Stanford. Monty's chums had set their caps at another, the highest there, and they never left Monty alone about it.

On "rushing" days, *we* would rush (although the word was meant the other way round) back from class, tear off our sensible skirts and pullovers, and put on the finest silks our parents had been able to buy for us. A fur coat was an enormous asset in spite of the warm weather. Hatted, gloved, but not in our right minds, we would be led into a drawing room whose curtains had been pulled against daylight. There, by candlelight, we would be received with gracious manners in full evening dress, passed from one hostess to the next, drink tea, and depart as mystified as when we came.

On the final fateful afternoon, all of us who still had hope (the ones who had continued to receive invitations) were told to remain in Hall, in our own rooms or where we could be found when our names were drawn. I sat with Monty and the gang in our study. We all sat and smoked (even Monty), chary of talking too much: it was unwise to give yourself away—supposing your choice didn't bid for you?—bids were kept a dead secret, and you were given three choices. If you had not made yourself too plain beforehand, who was to know that you did not get what you wanted? Our nerves were kept on the jump because there was no telling when a name would be called. Slips were pulled from a hat.

When a girl stood in the door and spoke my name, I got up and followed her along the empty corridors with the sensation that it was not the substantial me but an astral shell, which was obeying some unknown mysterious command. I stood before a table and was faced by three friends who showed no sign of recognition. I was asked to name the sorority of my choice. I gave the name, and the girl in the center looked down at a list. Yes, she said, that was all right. I was led down the corridor again and into another room where my new sisterhood waited. We were all under the shock of having touched Aladdin's lamp. Presently Monty came in. Then the chums, all but one. Even I mourned that lost sheep. So, Monty had gone against her mother's wishes; we were to go forward together in the autumn, as sisters.

X

SUMMER UNFOLDED ITSELF with a smile. Grandmother welcomed me with great affection and said that we must see that I enjoyed my holidays. She set about it at once. She gave small dinner parties at the hotel to include young men, sons of friends of hers from the East. Although these dinner dances could not have been of much interest to her, she planned and carried them out with spirit. Presently I was caught up in return invitations to San Diego, Coronado, Del Mar, and as far afield as Laguna; to house parties, to picnics by moonlight, to days of surfboard and water skis.

I was astonished at how much was going on and at the number of good-looking young men. Had it always been like this, but with me too young—too outside—to notice? As summer progressed, the groups broke up and fined down into paired couples. No time was lost among these couples to declare themselves, not in formal engagements—we were too young for that—but in temporary understandings. What it boiled down to was that the young man forfeited his fraternity pin, or ring, as a sort of lien on the girl; it gave him right-of-way to her evenings.

When the groups dwindled, I was left in possession of not one but two young men, the Alden brothers. One night, one, and the next, the other. I gathered that they did not know that they were each other's rival. The name of the older one was Thorn, and the younger one was called Thistle because they were so much alike. They looked alike and talked alike and drove the same sort of car, and after a while I found it more and more difficult to keep it clear and separate in my mind what I had done and where I had gone with which brother.

One night Thistle proposed, rather lightly. About a week later, after a dance in Coronado, Thorn stopped the car in the dark seldom-used street just above our house. He had something to ask me, he said. I looked down at my grand-mother's window—there was only flat lawn between it and us—the window showed no light but that did not mean that she was asleep. There was no mistaking the car I was in and it was open, one of those long seven-passenger Pack-ards which only the Alden family affected. Thorn was too serious to interrupt, and I was too nervous for comfort. "And so, could we consider ourselves engaged?" he said. I knew that if I agreed, it would mean sitting some long time, embraced, under my grandmother's nose. He was being awfully persistent—hadn't I refused him just the other day?

Thoughtless and quick, I said as much. The silence which followed made it plain that there had been a terrible mix-up. I had muddled up the brothers. Thorn's pride was hurt. He guessed now what Thistle had been up to all summer.

A rumpus must have broken out in the Alden household; at least there was no sign from either brother for the rest of the holidays.

I was left high and dry. Or I would have been if Edward Fowler had not stepped into the breach. College—or the time spent at college—had improved him enormously: he had grown tall, he danced smoothly, he wore his clothes well. He laughed about that first ball when he had refused to dance. "What an ass I was," he said, "last year."

Not long after my loss of the Alden brothers, Sonia asked me to lunch. She was on the crest of the wave and wanted to talk about it. Her mother had promised that she could go East to an aunt for the autumn and winter. And, meanwhile, she had had luck even here in La Playa. *The* most distinguished young Bostonian, Polly's nephew, David Wyatt Prentiss. Hadn't I noticed him? Tall and blond? "His father is a bishop," Sonia added with satisfaction.

It was a few nights later, when I was dancing with Edward Fowler at the hotel, that we met Sonia and her Bostonian. There was an exchange of partners and afterwards we sat together and ate lemon ices. Some people have about them a formality which can carry three names, and David Wyatt Prentiss was one of them. He had a long bony face and spoke very New England, but the elegance of the whole slender length of him belied any rudeness of early settlers. He seemed to have come from a gentler vein: the rich vein of the Established Church, High Church, Episcopalian, worldly. (I do not think this was all my imagination.)

Polly joined us for a time, so proud of her nephew and pleased that he was "in" with us. What a good foursome we made, she said, and invited us all to dine with her on Saturday night.

From then on, David Wyatt Prentiss was like the new word discovered and looked up in the dictionary: I came across him everywhere—on the tennis courts, at the beach, even in Grandmother's house where he had come with Polly for tea. David singled me out for interminable conversations. He said he could see that I had a serious turn of mind, far more serious than Sonia. I said it was only Sonia's manner that made him think that. "Manner is important," David said.

David talked about his plans and hopes for the future; they were bright and clear in his mind. He was going into the Church to follow in his father's footsteps; in fact, to walk into his father's boots. He foresaw a life of dedication. Somehow or other he got round to a partner to share this life. Did I think . . . ? Would a young woman consent to share it? Could I imagine . . . ?

"Yes," I said, about to add that there must be many.

He clasped my two hands in his and gave me a deep blue look from his eyes. Then he broke away and, with rapid strides, moved towards the house.

I could have called him back, stopped him before he reached my grandmother. But spreading over me was a curiosity—why not? I respected Sonia's taste. Of course it was bizarre to be engaged to a fledgling bishop, but why not? It wasn't as though these things were permanent or taken seriously. David had years of study ahead, and so had I. There would be time.

It was taken more seriously than I had bargained for. Instead of asking for my grandmother's permission, he laid before her the accomplished fact. She expressed her approval; Polly was delighted. David had made it a family matter; he would tell his parents—otherwise the engagement was to be private for the moment. Later on that afternoon, with a show of ritual he pinned over my heart his fraternity insignia, which was a miniature one, small as the slightest teardrop. He sealed the ceremony by saying that if he had given an impression of haste, it was because time was short. He had to leave for Boston the day after tomorrow. For him, there had been no actual haste; he had known from the first moment.

Polly and David were Grandmother's guests that night at the hotel. There was nothing to arouse suspicion in that. But I felt so different that I thought it might show.

Sonia came in with Edward Fowler. As usual we exchanged partners. Standing together at the end of the dance, I saw that Sonia's eyes had discovered the telltale insignia. Almost immediately she and Edward disappeared.

The next day in the afternoon David called to say good-bye. He was leaving very early in the morning. He and Polly were spending that night in San Diego with friends of hers, an arrangement of long standing. We strolled in the garden and David talked. He assured me of his happiness, of how he would treasure what had been entrusted to him. He spoke of the purity of maidenhood. I began to feel myself entwined in a Pre-Raphaelite tapestry when

David took a further plunge: now it was the sanctity of motherhood.

David went too fast for me. I felt both trapped and pressed. It was too soon and too late for me to take a stand. It would have to be done by letter and by time.

I let him do all the talking, which he seemed to take as his prerogative. He asked me to promise to write once a week (perhaps on Sunday evenings; then he could picture me as I wrote), and I wondered what on earth I should find to write about. The prospect seemed worse with him standing over my shoulder in his imagination. He kissed me goodbye in front of Grandmother, a rather bishoplike kiss on the brow.

"What a solemn young man," Grandmother said as soon as he was gone. From her expression and from the quick way she moved across the drawing room to straighten a book here, to touch a flower there, I knew that in her own mind she had relegated the affairs of my heart and my future to my own shoulders; my destiny was to be of my own choosing. (As long as I kept within reasonable bounds.)

Two days later I took the train for Stanford. I had in my handbag an envelope addressed in Sonia's handwriting. I took it out and unfolded the paper to look again at the message. Scrawled across the page, without a beginning or a signature, were the words *How could you?*

Whatever she meant by this—whether she thought I had treated her badly or only myself—I more than agreed with her.

XI

O<small>N THE TRAIN</small> I had resolved to be happy. That brief isolation which a train offers—cut off by movement, whirled forward to a new college year—seemed an ideal moment for resolutions. David was a problem that did not have to be dealt with at once; in the meantime, his pin would be a prize at Stanford, much as a scalp among Indian braves. Before me lay the mysterious coveted life of a sorority house. I gave the address to the taxi driver, and we turned into the tree-covered avenue.

At the house was a queue of cars and taxis and, on the steps, stacks of luggage. I was swept inside with a gaggle of girls and shouted greetings. Monty was in the hall; she told me she was already installed in a room with a chum.

The president of the house, a conventionally pretty girl whom I knew by sight, welcomed us all. She detained me by placing her hand on my arm, and when we were alone, she said that as I was the only girl coming into the house who had been up before the student body for a misdemeanor, it had been decided that I should share a room with her for the first term.

We went upstairs together. The room was on the third floor, at the top of the house, sunny, and overlooking the front. There were two single beds, two dressing tables, and not much closet space. "All of us," she said, "have bunks on the screened-in sleeping porch. No one, unless she is ill, sleeps in her room. This is a dressing room, really."

In the middle of hanging up my clothes, I stopped and sat on the bed and lit a cigarette. Why had I come here? Sheeplike behavior, running with the crowd. I had liked some of the girls. Now I realized that the girls I had liked had been in their last year and were gone. During those rushing parties it had not occurred to me to wonder how so many girls could live in one house with a single bathroom to each floor; in our heads at that time was only the hysterical fear of being left out. At best, this might turn out to be like a cramped house party where one had to grab for the amenities. I did not yet know that the raw material—we new girls—was expected to give way on every point: *You first; I'll have a bath some other time.* The communal rooms downstairs were spacious and comfortable and agreeably furnished. There were niches and corners for study but these places were usually occupied. There was no privacy anywhere, least of all in my bedroom, which was like a commander's tent with the coming and going of girls on missions for the president.

Every girl at Stanford had an interview with Dean Yost about her course of study. It was not necessary to name your major subject until the third year, but Dean Yost liked you to have an idea. Quite forgetful of shaping my mind to that of a bishop's wife, I thought only of my gasoline and my fortune; I chose science, wavering between chemistry and physics. "Splendid," Dean Yost said. The preparation for both was the same in the first years.

I had an affectionate letter from my grandmother enclosing a check for a thousand dollars. She wrote that she had no idea what money I would need. None of her daughters had gone to college. My father and uncles had spent a good deal and now, since the war, the price of everything had gone up. I should let her know if I ran short.

I had a comfortable balance at the bank and deposited the check along with it. There was nothing much I spent money on except books and cigarettes and an occasional snack in Palo Alto. I bought cigarettes (Chesterfields) by the carton so that I wouldn't run out. Before long I was supplying all those who did, because you can't refuse anyone a package of cigarettes. After a while, the girls just helped themselves; no one bothered to ask. I couldn't keep cigarettes even by hiding them under my clothes. Hal said I should do what he did: change to Camels. He found that women refused them because they were so strong. I did and my cartons remained intact. No one could complain that I was being mean, merely that my taste had roughened.

One of the first days back Hal telephoned that he had

press tickets to Galli-Curci in San Francisco; would I come? I said "yes" without remembering that I had to ask permission. The president came into our room while I was dressing and wanted to know where I was going. She said it would be all right this once; that is, if I never let it happen again—without asking.

It was Hal's last year and he was working hard. He did not take time off to go to San Francisco unless it was for some outstanding performance to which he had press tickets. He would take me on these jaunts which ranged through opera to Ring Lardner to Borotra and Suzanne Lenglen, under floodlights. And because we went so rarely, we made an occasion of our Chianti dinners. We went to the best of the Italian restaurants and always to a private room upstairs (probably that was the speakeasy part). Hal needed space and quiet because he had to write up whatever we had seen and turn it in that night at the newspaper office. He would jot down a skeleton of highlights over a cocktail. Then during dinner he seemed able to write with one hand and eat with the other and discuss the evening with me, all at the same time.

Hal's manner to me did not change when he saw the fraternity pin I wore. He asked if it was a Stanford guy, and when I said "no," I think he forgot all about it.

Gone forever was the happy independence of Freshman Hall. I saw even more of Monty than when we were roommates. We ate together, most of our classes were the same, sorority sisters flocked together on the campus, and on the sleeping porch I had been put in the bunk directly over her. Because of this, she always knew when I went to bed.

If I was very late, she made a point of speaking to me to show that she was aware of what was going on.

At the House everything one did was known and commented on. And very soon it was clear that a conscientious effort was being directed against us—the new sisters. The intention was to groom and mold us into the sorority pattern. This pattern involved our persons as well as our actions. Clothes were supposed to be chic and rich, not the harum-scarum flannel skirt and pullover, hair to be waved and set in the corrugated fashion, makeup in evidence but discreet, nails manicured and buffed. As for actions, we were supposed to be as active as possible, to take part in as many college affairs as we could get into, and never to forget that we were leaders. If we dated men, they should be fraternity men.

My hair was cut in a short shingle. I was told to let it grow. I was warned against being seen too often with Hal or Eddy Cavendish; neither was a fraternity man. Dainty was all right. I happened to know that he was more than all right; he was a DKE. Nothing was better than a DKE unless it was two DKEs.

It was no hardship dating Dainty. He had dropped the white tie of last year, and now his idea of an evening was a race up the inland road in a Stutz Bearcat piled high with good fellows (with me somewhere underneath) to the latest, hottest roadhouse. It didn't seem to matter to them that I was the only woman present. They treated me as a sort of mascot, and David's pin was a DKE pin so I was, by promise, at one with them.

You *were* encouraged to date fraternity men, but if you went out with three or four and didn't share them, you got only resentment. Even so, I did not dream of badgering the boys into taking a sorority sister; her hair would stand on end at the drinking and the floor-show girls who sat at our table. She would cramp the evening.

In any case, the fact that the sorority house had taken it upon itself to dictate my friendships put me into a rebellious state of mind. Had Hal or Eddy been available, I would have seen them more than ever. As it was, Hal was sunk in work and Eddy had gone underground to compose that symphony of his, based now on the Civil War—a hotch-potch of *The Red Badge of Courage* and Walt Whitman.

I did not let my hair grow or get a permanent wave.

The House told me to try out for a college play. As this seemed a reasonable request, I did. And got the part. This cheered them up a good deal. Then, when I was made captain of the hockey team, I was accepted as almost one of themselves.

Just before Christmas, Dainty and the gang heard about a new roadhouse to try out. It was difficult to find, off the main road, and none of us knew how far the turning was beyond San Jose. It was bitterly cold in the open car in spite of a raccoon coat thrown over our laps. We had a flask of whisky and one of gin to help keep us warm. Both tasted raw and burned the lining of the stomach without sending the heat farther. We drove into, and were shooed out from, several large farmyards. When at last we did find the roadhouse, it was dimly lit and sinister-looking as though in wait for a mob attack. In the darkness at the side of the house two men unloaded crates from a truck.

Inside, you could see that it was a farmhouse not entirely converted. There was a dining room, quite empty, with a number of tables with red-and-white checked tablecloths, and a good-sized iron stove, red-hot. We gathered to it like steel to a magnet. A man in a business suit came in and said that the restaurant wasn't open. The opening night was to be on New Year's Eve. When he saw our reluctance to leave, he said the cook would make us a dish of spaghetti Bolognese, and there was Chianti. We approved lustily; nothing could have pried us from that stove. The spaghetti was good; the Chianti tasted peculiar, but then, all drink tasted peculiar. We did not drink the less for that. The time came when there seemed no more excuse to stay on.

I did not feel the cold until the car began to move, and then it was a sting across the face. The stars danced in the sky and I realized that my head was on the back of the seat and I was staring straight up. I did not think to move it. The boys sang. I touched my forehead with my fingers and they came away wet—a cold sweat, I said to myself with satisfaction.

We stopped at the dark sorority house. The boys wouldn't understand that it was too late to come in, so I fooled them by slipping in at the door and bolting it behind me.

Climbing up to my bunk, I stepped on Monty's arm, which made her furious. I stayed up there as long as I could. I turned on my side and I was falling, flat on my back and the whole room rocked. Sitting up was best, but it was so cold. I climbed down again and went to the bathroom and there I was suddenly sick. Monty was at the door when I came out. She said she thought something was the matter. I said I was catching flu and was going to sleep inside.

The president shook me awake and then felt my forehead.

"It *is* hot," she said. Monty had come to her with a garbled story about my catching flu and about smelling of drink and being sick in the bathroom. "Which of it is true?"

I said I had been drinking, but not on campus grounds.

I had broken college rules by being intoxicated on campus grounds.

I said that I hadn't been intoxicated.

"Being sick is a form of intoxication." She would have to put the matter before the Student Committee.

I ran into Dainty after English history and he said, did I know what we had drunk last night? I told him that whatever it was, it was being aired in front of a women's committee.

"Grape juice mixed with ether," Dainty said. One of the boys had brought a bottle back. This morning, and without the Bolognese sauce, there was no mistaking it.

So his DKEs would swear I had not been drunk on alcohol?

"Sure," he said. He looked so eager that I had to say I was joking. "Even a committee," I said, "would think Chianti more blameless than ether."

A fortnight later we broke up for the Christmas holidays. My grandmother had gone East to spend them with some of her children, and so I was supposed to go to the Hamiltons in Pasadena. A few hours before I left, the president told me the decision of the Student Committee: I was to be put on *social probation*.

I asked what that meant.

It meant that I was forbidden to speak to students on the

campus, she said, and that I would have to be very careful in the future. I was allowed to stay on in college on sufferance.

"And if they speak to me?"

"They won't," she said, and explained that my name would be put up on the boards.

I asked how long it would last.

Indefinitely, the president said, depending on my behavior.

The holidays passed in a flash, and I was back on the night train to San Francisco. In Pasadena the Hamiltons, the dances, the dinner parties, going to the theater—everything had been gay as larks. Once Jay had caught a sad look on my face and put it down to homesickness for Grandmother. He offered me his plane to fly East in, and I made the mistake of saying I didn't know how to fly. "It's easier than driving a car," he said. It looked as though I were in for another daredevil dare until I swore that I was having such a good time with them that I didn't want to go East.

The social probation did weigh on my mind, and now that I was almost back at Stanford, I tried to imagine what college life would be like if I couldn't speak to anyone.

Social probation opened doors which would have been closed to me in the ordinary way. Professors and postgraduates (who were not controlled by student rule) were indignant and up in arms. They saw my name on the boards; they realized the punishment and sought me out. To them it was a matter of principle. They believed that no student should be treated like a social leper.

After class the professor walked across to the library or to the coffee shop with me—did I have time for a cup of coffee?—he wanted to discuss a certain point with me. I was invited to evening parties, too, to dinner or to drinks in the professors' houses. This turn of events did not help my cause; it enraged the student body that their punishment should flower into something else, but it made all the difference to me.

Dainty shifted his seat to sit next to me in English and English history—the two subjects we both took—because we were allowed to speak in classrooms, before and after class. It wasn't the same. Dainty wasn't a man for talk, but to do things with. Hal I could meet in Palo Alto and we could drive up to San Francisco, but it needed at least a Barrymore to get House permission for a late night. Time spent in the sorority house was the worst, because no one spoke except to say things like "Pass the sugar, please." Sometimes the president talked to me in our room, and in quite a friendly tone. I do not know why she felt able to unless her position placed her above rules.

The time came when intercollegiate hockey matches were marked up for the next month, and it was announced that the team should go into training. As captain, I was told to see to it that the players did not smoke. This was a contingency that had not occurred to me. I had signed on for hockey only because a sport was obligatory. I wasn't interested in matches. Couldn't I resign from the team?

Not unless I gave up hockey, the sports coach said.

I had to have a credit for sports to pass my second year, didn't I?

She agreed.

I thought it over for several days. Smoking was the one pleasure left and my only resource on long evenings at the sorority house. I did not see why I should give it up simply because I had got on the team. It wasn't as though women's hockey meant anything to anyone.

I went again to the coach and quite frankly stated my position. And I said that I had strong objections to having to snoop after other people to see that they, too, did not smoke. Surprisingly enough, she was sympathetic. I could not switch to calisthenics—the class was too advanced; swimming was the same—the class had already passed certain tests. But I could, if I liked, take up archery. Some of the girls were pretty good by now; I'd have to put my back into it (she laughed at this joke); she would not be able to pass me unless I came up to certain marksman standards.

I decided to do this, and I was delighted to find that the full-length bow took strength and art to handle with precision. It was not a child's game.

I had not foreseen the impact that my abandoning hockey would make on my unspeaking sisters. They glowered; they glared at me. The president took me off upstairs. I was a bitter disappointment to them all, she said. By throwing away my captaincy, I had let down the House. I had failed those who believed in me.

"*Failed whom?*" I said. But she did not answer.

"Each one of us is expected . . ."

"The most I can expect," I said, "or hope for, is a *modus vivendi.*"

She looked at me rather blankly. "You can go now," the president said. "You know how we feel."

I had a friend in the enemy's camp, Mary Farnham. She was a sorority sister and a postgraduate; consequently, she lived in Palo Alto. We were good friends, and, technically, I was able to see and talk to her. She was an ex-president of the House and an ex-committee member of the student body, so she knew the ins and outs of everything. She still had a lot of influence—negative influence, she called it. She could do nothing about reinstating me, she said. The committee was determined to continue the social probation until the end of term because, as it had not proved effective on the campus, it would at least make it impossible for me to be initiated into the sorority.

I said that initiation was the least of my worries.

She pounced on me then; I must never say that. If it got about that I didn't *care*, goodness knew what they'd think up. She was beginning to believe I didn't realize the seriousness of my situation. If I did, I would never have given up being captain of hockey. I was an idiot not to have consulted her first. Now the only activity I had to my credit was the part in the play. I must stick to that, no matter what happened. Then she told me that I was stirring up a new hornet's nest by going about everywhere with the good-looking young professor from Princeton.

"*He* goes about with me," I said. "He is agog with the savagery of women students toward each other. He likes to watch their faces as we approach."

*   *   *

Some days before the big game, Mary took me aside and asked what my plans were for the big night.

"What everybody is doing," I said, "dancing in San Francisco."

It would be wiser to stay at home, she said. If anything should happen—anything at all—I would be done for.

I did not see what could happen. I was going with Hal. He never drank too much and he wasn't flighty. He had booked a table on the roof garden of the Mark Hopkins. What could be more respectable and aboveboard?

Mary was worried about my getting back. It was against the social probation rules for Hal to drive me on the campus. What if I couldn't find a taxi in Palo Alto at that time of night? Presently she said she had an idea. She would ask the president if I could stay at her house in Palo Alto. It would be all right if she made herself responsible for me.

Hal picked me up at Mary's house. Coming down the stairs, I heard Hal promise Mary that he'd look after me like a mother hen. He had a Sunday look—the usual impression he gave was that he had just come out of a high wind.

There weren't many cars on the road. "Everybody's already there," Hal said. "They've been raising Cain ever since the game ended. We've won again." And he said that he had called in at the newspaper office to find out.

Hal parked his car and we went into a soda-fountain place. Hal was hungry and ordered club sandwiches and gingerales. Dinner would be late at the hotel and we were supposed to meet Gordon French and a girl here. I knew him, didn't I?

"The quiet DKE," I said.

"He's on the paper," Hal said, as though his being out with a fraternity man needed explaining. He took a pint of rye from his pocket and poured out a base for the ginger-ale. We were in a booth at the back, the place was dim and quiet, and Hal watched the door in the looking glass. We hadn't seen each other for a long time. The latest news, he said, was that his mother had taken a furnished apartment in San Francisco and expected him to spend his weekends with her. Ever since she had told him about the adoption, she'd hung on to him as though he were trying to escape.

Gordon French came in with a pretty dark girl from Berkeley. They sat down and Hal offered them a drink, which they both refused. The girl "didn't" and Gordon said he had to drive.

We all got into Gordon's car, which was a Cadillac sedan. For a while we had to move at a crawl behind a line of cars; then, quite suddenly, the congestion cleared. The girl in front turned round to say something to me. I leaned forward and at that instant I saw out of the corner of my eye a car down a perpendicular side street, not stopping at the stop sign, rushing on to us.

It was dark and I was uncomfortable. When I tried to move, it hurt. I realized it was dark because my eyes were shut. I opened them and saw Hal's face, quite close. His face went away and I saw only trouser legs. I was lying in the gutter. I turned my head and saw a policeman holding back a crowd of people. Of course, we had been in a car accident. I remembered.

Hal came back with another policeman, who leaned down and asked if I felt strong enough to get up. "Naturally," I said. Presently I felt myself being helped up, Hal on one side and the policeman on the other. As I stood up, a shower of glass fell to the pavement. They put me in a car. After a while Hal and the policeman came back, and Hal said we were being taken to his mother's apartment.

When we were alone going up in the elevator, Hal said he had had to give a San Francisco address; otherwise the police would not have let us go. They were sending one of their doctors round to examine us. Red tape and a question of insurance.

Hal's mother opened the door. "You've come, after all!" It was a happy exclamation, and she did not seem to notice my presence at first. Hal said we had been in a car accident. She opened her mouth and screamed. I jumped at the suddenness. Hal put his arm round her and led her into the bedroom and shut the door.

I went over to the looking glass. My hair was like a wet mop; Hal said the policeman had thrown water over me to bring me round. I combed it and powdered my nose. The front of my dress was soaking and I felt frozen through.

Hal came out of the bedroom and I asked him what had happened to Gordon French and the girl.

"Perfectly all right," he said. "Not a scratch."

"And the other car? Why didn't it stop?"

Hal looked astonished. Hadn't I heard? It was a stolen car; the police had been chasing it. That's why the police were there, on the spot. And in spite of them, he said, the thieves got away in the crowd.

Mrs. Forbes came out of the bedroom. She was calmed

now but she didn't take her eyes off Hal, and as soon as the doctor came, she took him straight into the bedroom to examine her son. Afterwards, he examined me in the sitting room. When I took off my dress, I was surprised at the color of my thighs; they were black-and-blue and had been cut as well. The doctor pulled out some splinters of glass. He found that I had a couple of ribs broken—which, he said, sounded worse than it was: a minor injury that would heal by itself. The ribs didn't even need to be strapped. "You're fine," he said, "and your young man is fine. You're both lucky to be alive." At the station he'd heard that the Cadillac had turned over twice before it smashed. It was so smashed that it would have to be shoveled up.

As soon as the doctor left, Hal telephoned Mary. She was in a state about it all, but she showed herself sensible, too. Under no circumstances should I try to come back in the morning in evening dress. She would bring my day clothes to me by the first train and we'd go back together.

The doctor had given me a sleeping pill and I was beginning to feel the effects of it. I was supposed to sleep on the divan but there were no signs of covers. Mrs. Forbes had not come out of the bedroom again. I gathered that she was cross with Hal for bringing a girl with him. I asked Hal what to do and he brought me his topcoat; he nodded toward the bedroom and shrugged. It was plain that he did not want to bother his mother with it. Almost at once I was dead asleep.

Some time in the middle of the night I was dragged awake by doorbells and lights and more policemen—a different lot from our earlier ones. These had discovered our address in the doctor's report in connection with the accident, and they had come to arrest us for stealing the other car. They had seen the wreck and knew it wasn't possible to have been in the Cadillac and live. Hal finally got them to go by giving them the station number and name of the policeman who had pulled us out of the Cadillac. I was asleep again before Hal had shut the door.

Mary came for me very early. I changed my clothes and we caught a train straight back. We saw no one we knew, not even when we got off at Palo Alto. I told Mary the whole story on the train. When we got to her house, she said to go upstairs and get into a hot bath and she'd bring up some coffee. She was furious with Hal's mother for leaving me all night without a blanket. I found it difficult to step into the tub with my bad legs, but the warmth was a relief once I was in the water.

Mary brought the coffeepot and two cups. She was angry all over again when she saw my black thighs and the cuts; she was angry with fate, this time. "Really," she said, "it's *too bad.*"

When she thought what some girls got away with at college!—they had affairs and goodness knew what—but because they followed an accepted pattern, nobody noticed. They got off scot-free. Whereas I . . . I stuck out like a sore thumb; no matter what innocent trick I got caught up with, it turned out to be a booby trap—ether, a car smash— and in the end it all looked worse than whatever it was other people did. "It all *looks* so bad. Look at yourself now," she said. "You *look* worse than a girl who has spent a night with a lover."

Mary went back to the sorority house with me that night and had dinner there, a guest of honor. She sat between the president and me and talked to us both, making an easy bridge. Before she left, she saw me into bed in the bedroom to avoid the painful climb up into a top bunk. I had caught a chill, she told the president. There was an epidemic of colds and flu about.

I tried to read a novel but my mind wasn't in it. I knew I should be writing to David—it had become my Sunday chore—but my ribs were beginning to hurt; I turned out the light and lay flat.

I did wake up with a streaming cold (the outcome of Mary's fib?). It was a wonder that it hadn't come on before, after the freezing night, but better late than never—what a blessing to have an obvious excuse to stay in bed!

Mary had made me see that at all costs I must conceal my cuts and bumps; no matter how innocent I was, a car smash would be held against me. I worried about archery with my ribs—could I do it without giving myself away?— it was three times a week; if I missed today, the ribs might be healed by Wednesday.

Mary had put the fear of God into me. When I did get up, I tried to pretend I was invisible and it worked quite well. No one took any notice; I avoided the professors; I spent my time in the library. My energies were spent in getting myself from one class to the next without limping or wincing. Pulling the bow in archery was painful, but, thank heavens, there was a match on, and it was turn and turn about with long waits in between.

Dean Yost sent for me. My heart shot into my throat when she said, "A pretty kettle of fish." Was it true I was taking a course marked on the study list *for postgraduates?*

I said that she had recommended it herself.

So she had. Well, she was sorry. I would have to drop it. Some students had objected that if a second-year student got credit for a postgraduate course, it automatically invalidated the course for the postgraduates. She had taken the matter up with the university president, and he had decided against me.

Dean Yost said again that she was sorry. And I said that it didn't matter (I was so relieved that it was nothing worse). I had extra credits, thanks to her.

Two days later in archery—it was the semifinals and still I hadn't been eliminated—the booby trap was sprung: I pulled back the bow, I was steadying the aim, and something snapped, something inside me. I must have fainted dead away. I came to with the coach waving a small bottle under my nose, and I almost laughed that this sturdy stocky woman, of all people, should be in possession of smelling salts. By a lucky coincidence, she said, a doctor was in the gymnasium; she'd sent a girl for him.

From the moment the doctor arrived, events swam one into the other. He examined me and somehow it was in my bedroom at the sorority house. I was afraid he would find out about my ribs because he was very much interested in my chest. He was gone for a while and then he came back into the room with the president, who gathered up my brush and comb and night things. He drove me to Mary's house.

She was standing at the door and took me upstairs into the guest room where the bed had been made up for me. Mary helped me get into bed; she pulled down the blinds. The doctor had told her it was pleurisy and he wanted me kept quiet and in the dark.

This began a strange time, because there was never a separate day or night. The blinds and heavy curtains were always tight shut. Sometimes there was a dim light in the far corner of the room and an elderly woman sat there, knitting. She would give me mushy things to eat or pills to swallow or take my temperature. I asked to see Mary and she said I wasn't supposed to see anyone. I may have had a fever because I could feel the heat against the pillow. I don't know how long this lasted—several days; it might have been a week. I slept almost all the time; and that, too, was strange.

Then, one day, I felt I would never sleep again. I lay in the dark and fidgeted. As soon as the nurse came in, I told her that I felt all right and was going to get up. She looked at her watch. "It won't be long now," she said. I thought of the March Hare, or was it the Mad Hatter who dipped his watch in the tea? What had *the time* got to do with it?

She placed a tray on my lap. For the first time there was something solid to eat. A breast of chicken and mashed potatoes. The nurse didn't stay. What I had wanted to ask was what had happened to Mary? Why didn't she come in?

The nurse had come back for the tray, but instead of stopping at the bed, she walked to the windows, flung back the curtains and snapped up the blinds. Sun blazed in. I turned my head from the brightness. Standing in the open door was an apparition. In hat and coat, holding her ebony stick—my grandmother.

"How did you get here?" I said.

"By train." Her answer made my question sound as foolish as it was. "Yesterday."

"*But why?*"

It was most inconsiderate, she said. She had been sent for. She stepped into the room and stood at the foot of the bed, looking down at me. "I was told you were ill."

She went to the window and opened it at the top. "The students who met me at the train said you are no longer ill but you have been expelled from college." She went back to the foot of the bed and spoke rapidly now. They called themselves the Student Committee: a talkative, hysterical lot. If she had not gone to Dean Yost, she would not have been able to make out the situation.

Grandmother glanced at her watch. "The committee has expelled you from college," she said, "and the members seem afraid to see you. They sent for me so that I would take you home at once. Your things have been packed and are at the station. Our train leaves in half an hour. The taxi is at the door." She said that she would wait for me in it.

We caught the train and were shown into a private drawing room. That was the worst to bear, being alone with Grandmother. She was icy and spoke only when I asked her a question. She had opened a book at once and had begun to read. I sat and looked out of the window and then I looked at Grandmother's hat which had a high straight crown with a wide buckle as decoration, like the Pilgrim Fathers. I could not stand it any longer. I interrupted her reading. I asked, I said I would like to know *why* the Student Committee had acted as they did.

She held her finger in her place in the book. There were articles in the San Francisco papers, she said. She had been shown them. About car thieves having been caught and about a motor car accident which had taken place and my name had been mentioned. She herself had pointed out that I had not stolen the car, but had merely been a passenger in the damaged one. They had said that that was the point: I was supposed to be with someone else, a young man who was known to be serious; instead of which, I had been driving about with a DKE. Grandmother hesitated for a moment. She knew, she said, that my David was a DKE, but the committee had insisted that this DKE must have been pretty drunk to get in the way of a car which must have been conspicuous because of the police siren behind it.

I said that I had been with Hal, in the back. Hadn't his name been mentioned?

Grandmother shook her head. The student committee insisted that the car accident was simply the last straw.

"If only I could have talked to them."

"That is what they were afraid of," Grandmother said. They had told her that, each time, I had explained everything away; turned black into white.

Grandmother went back to her book and read until it was dark. She rang the bell and ordered dinner to be brought in.

I couldn't eat very much. Grandmother looked at me with curiosity as though I were a familiar plant which had burst into an unknown leaf. "They tell me," she said, "that you break the laws of our country, as well, that you have taken to drink. Do you *enjoy* muddling your wits?"

I could not reply.

XII

"YOU HAVE MADE your bed and now you must lie in it" was what my grandmother said to me on my first day at home. It was a cold empty bed. My friends were away, Sonia in the East, Mary Manning at college; they were all gone. There was nothing to do, and I had no heart for doing it.

My grandmother paid little attention to me. We both needed to replenish our forces, and I think this was her way. The shock must have been even greater for her than for me. I had had warnings and signs; she had had nothing but irreproachable scholastic reports. She went about her own affairs, in silence, as though I weren't, strictly speaking, there.

David had released me from my engagement. I had written him at once what had happened at the university; and from the speed of his reply, he must have sat down to his desk without hesitation. It was a calm, reasoned, lengthy letter expressing sorrow at my misfortunes and hope for the future. Reluctantly (he wrote) he must agree with me: a woman who had been evicted from a university for wildness would not make a suitable wife to a dedicated man. He remained, etc.

Mrs. Randall telephoned: No, *not* to speak to Grandmother. She wanted to talk to me. She'd heard that *the worst had happened*. I must tell her *all*, everything! Could I come to lunch?—tomorrow?—just the two of us. From her voice, Mrs. Randall expected excitement. I knew that my story would fall short and would disappoint her—what was it, after all?—and the last thing I wanted was to talk to Sonia's mother about myself. I said I was sorry but I wasn't going out nowadays. "Oh, you poor thing," she said, "is it to be so soon?"

I tried to convince Mrs. Randall that what she had in mind was quite wrong. I do not know that I did. Her voice got colder and farther away. She said, "So *that's* your story," and she hung up.

Jay Hamilton wrote that he had heard of my harsh treatment from Mrs. Montgomery. He wrote a sympathetic letter: we high-spirited ones were often misunderstood. Would I like to come to them for a few days? He wanted to talk to me about it; perhaps something could be done.

My grandmother urged me to go. I think she wanted a few days without me underfoot. She said that Jay Hamilton was the right person to give advice—the same thing had happened to him when he was at college; it had broken his father's heart.

Jay listened to my story with complete attentiveness—and this was one of his greatest qualities: the still, absolute absorption in a problem. He asked innumerable questions about student self-government; the mechanics of it seemed to fascinate him. He laughed aloud at the student body slogan: *Alcohol and gasoline do not mix.* He wanted to know if President Hoover had coined it. His election must have been a feather in Stanford's cap. He was a sort of godfather to the college, wasn't he, with his house right on the campus?

Jay persuaded me that I would feel better if I had a chance to speak to Dean Yost and to the president of the university. He packed me off with Hawkins in the plane to strike while the iron was still red-hot.

An interview with the president was difficult to come by; I was kept waiting half the morning. He was a tall cadaverous figure, formal in dress and stiff in manner. With an unexpected glint in his eye, he began by saying that I had turned the tables on him; it was usually *his* place to summon the student. He looked down at a sheet of paper on his desk. If I had come about my recent expulsion, he could do nothing for me. Matters of conduct were dealt with by the student body. My case was, consequently, out of his hands. He stood up, and I found myself walking out the door.

I was shown at once into Dean Yost's inner office. She received me affectionately. She seemed genuinely sorry. Before I could say a word, she had made it clear that my fate was outside her powers, beyond her reach, both at the time and now. She offered as cold comfort the fact that I was not alone. Some two hundred and fifty students had been expelled in a radical, large-scale, spring cleaning: every student who might conceivably have put a foot wrong.

All of Dainty's gang were out. And Dean Yost mentioned other names, a few women whom I knew to have been brilliant students, cases sadder than mine, she explained. They had been academic material, destined for the teaching profession, and their parents had made heavy financial sacrifices to send them to a university. Now they would be unable to get in anywhere.

Did she mean that we would not be taken by California or Southern California? Surely anybody who lived in the state could go to the state university?

Dean Yost shook her head. No university, she said, would accept a student who had been cast out from another recognized institution—except, perhaps, under special recommendation. And here, she said, she could help. (She had already proposed this to my grandmother, but at a time when she was too upset to make up her mind.) She knew my abilities and she would feel quite easy about recommending me to Vassar. She believed she could get me in. She would not endorse my going to another coeducational college. It would have to be Vassar or nothing.

The irony that Vassar should be offered now and as a result of punishment! Vassar had always been my dearest ambition, opposed stubbornly by my grandmother; she would not hear of it. For some unfathomable reason, my grandmother had been determined on a coeducational college for me. Equally, now, Dean Yost was against it. Why? I wondered. Why did each feel so certain, holding the opposite view?

In my bones I felt that my grandmother would not change: it would have to be the nothing, and *nothing* was what I dreaded. Not that I hankered after a formal education. But unlike Sonia, I did not feel ready for life. The thought of it made me quake. How did one go about it? What did one *do*?

I thanked Dean Yost and said I would let her know what my grandmother decided.

Jay Hamilton had been right: I did feel better for having come back. Dean Yost's offer had made a world of difference to my self-respect; she could not have paid me a higher compliment. And the corrosive poison of social probation was blown away as though by a fresh breeze. On the way from the president's office, I saw a group of friends who belonged to the sorority on the opposite side of the avenue from mine, the only one we admitted as a rival. They hailed me from a distance, even ran to meet me. When they heard I had come back only for the day, they insisted that I lunch at their house. It came as a revelation, this new freedom to speak and be spoken to. It wasn't true that I had lost all my friends. They waited for me outside Dean Yost's office and we all walked together up the shaded avenue. My friends were fierce with indignation. If I had been *one of them,* this would not have happened! *They* would have managed me. I wondered.

I did not cross over to my sorority or say goodbye to the sisters. Directly after lunch, I took a taxi to the airport.

I had dinner and spent the night in Pasadena before returning to La Playa. The tale of my interviews tickled Jay's fancy. While I was away, he had inquired about the president of Stanford. It seemed he had spent most of his life engaged in missionary work, latterly in the Middle East (if he had known this, Jay might have suggested skipping him). He was a friend of Hoover's; perhaps he was a political appointment? But it was the spring cleaning which brought sparks to Jay's eyes. Partly, I think it was the relief that I was one of a crowd, one in two hundred and fifty. "You can absolve yourself," he said, "you've been caught in the wheels of big machinery."

With my grandmother it was a different matter: the general aspect of my eviction did not interest her, nor to her mind did it lessen my guilt. Quite simply, I had broken the rules and I was paying for it.

Grandmother had received me back with her full attention as though this were my real return home. We had had a pleasant dinner together, avoiding serious topics. Afterwards, she led the way to the shadowy sweet-scented patio. I told her what Dean Yost had said about Vassar. Her answer was that I had forfeited my right to higher education. She waved aside the large-scale spring cleaning. "Numbers do not mitigate what you have done.

"We are not going to dwell on the past," she said. "We must catch up with the present." While I was away, she had thought it over; she was quite willing for me to continue to live on here with her. (What else *could* she have imagined?) My heart began to pound as it had after my escape from the volcano crater. I touched the ear that had ached.

Grandmother was saying that probably I would marry soon—that is, if what she had heard at Stanford about my predilection for young men was true. In the meantime, she had arranged for me to take some lessons—it would help to have something definite to do—three hours a week of French, three hours a week learning to paint with water color. (Didn't she know that I preferred Spanish and was only interested in working in oils?) "Oils are far easier," she said, "because you can scrape off your mistakes." For that very reason, she wanted me to try water colors. It would do me good to be engaged in something where my mistakes would remain visible, there in front of me.

Both of my teachers were old ladies, friends of Grandmother, whom I had met but had never noticed. They were shadowy figures; even while I worked and talked with them, they did not gain in substance. They were used up, burned out, worn away. I sensed some overwhelming tragedy, followed by grinding years of the monotony of making ends meet. My own mood did not add anything. We plodded through the hours and the motions.

I sought refuge in the Greek ice-cream parlor because of the private booths there where I could sit and drink black coffee and smoke, safe from Grandmother and her friends. I told myself I went there to think; actually, it was for anonymity. I enjoyed the time I spent there. Also I enjoyed watching and smelling the sea. I enjoyed driving a car, alone, and very fast.

One day Uncle Andrew came to lunch; he was on his way to the Wednesday afternoon matinee of the San Diego Repertory Company, and he suggested that I come with him. The thought of a tête-à-tête about college daunted me, but it was bound to come sooner or later.

We went out to the big open Delage. With a half-ironic, half-gallant sweep of the arm, Andrew offered me the driving seat. I took the wheel and gave myself up to handling of the unfamiliar powerful car. Andrew showed me how to double-clutch in changing down; it was smoother. Soon I got the feel of the car and we sailed along the coast, blown by the sea air and the smell of kelp. I parked the car and Andrew opened my door as though he were presenting me with a new world. He even said, "I'm going to show you something you don't know." We went down narrow streets and into nameless shops. "Housewives forget that San Diego is a port." He threw the words over his shoulder. He chose a camembert here, bamboo shoots and soya sauce there, spaghetti in long sheaves, coffee which had been roasted black. It was as gay as Christmas.

We were in the theater before the curtain went up. It was *The Last of Mrs. Cheney* and swept me quite out of myself. At the end, I was dazed to be back in San Diego sitting next to Andrew, to be someone expelled from college whom Grandmother did not approve of. Afterwards we were talking about the play, so that I didn't notice we weren't on the usual road until Andrew stopped on a point above the sea. The sun had sunk into the water, leaving a burnished streak in the sky and a radiance over everything. He said he could not bear monkey tricks with hip flasks in restaurants. He poured us each a dry martini and said we were on our way to a place famous for its steaks.

At the end of dinner Andrew spoke for the first time about me. He said that Grandmother had given him a full report about Stanford; we would not discuss it, because I must be fed up with it all. But he was worried about one thing. He was quite aware that my grandmother was not easy—she had an unbending side—he was afraid I might decide to run away. If I did, would I promise to let him know before I took the definite step? I could telephone him at any hour, day or night.

I thought it very funny that Andrew should think I would make such a dramatic gesture. It had never occurred to me. Perhaps it was the logical, courageous thing to do? To seek my fortune? To get a job? I began to think about it.

Would I promise? Andrew asked again. And I did.

From that evening, my position appeared to me increasingly ignoble. Here I was, stuck in a mindless Victorian pattern, dabbling in water colors and French while I waited to be married. (A vase of roses on a mahogany table—"Aren't the white highlights exciting?") Surely my life held more in store than that?

It was too early in the year to swim; I did not feel like going to the club to play tennis: everybody there knew me. Those who had heard about my fall did not know quite what stand to take; those who hadn't heard asked why I was at home. I avoided old haunts, and in spite of the ice-cream parlor and walks along the beach, I found myself more often than not hanging about the house. I tried to make myself appear busy and, if I couldn't succeed in that, to look unconcerned. My stoic presence exasperated my grandmother. She may have thought it her duty to poke an inert lump into awareness, or she may even have felt that this disgrace had hit her harder than me and she was impelled to redress the balance. She never left me alone: she prodded me about the ingratitude of my behavior, about sloth (getting up early had always been a struggle; now I saw no reason for it), about self-indulgence (to her, this was drink). The more wooden my face, the sharper her accusations grew; these, by necessity, took the form of monologues because I never answered back.

One night when she had gone off to a concert in San Diego with friends, she left me in a particularly bruised state. My grandmother was a punctual woman. Out of nervousness—not to keep other people waiting—that evening she had put on her hat and coat and was standing with her gloves in her hands a good twenty minutes before her friends were expected. From a compulsive sense of politeness, I stood with her. She took it as an ideal moment for a lecture. It relieved her irritation at having to wait herself.

As soon as she had driven off, I got a suitcase down from the top shelf of my closet. It was a small overnight case my grandmother had given me on my last birthday (I would leave with the minimum of worldly goods, just enough to get into a hotel). On it I noticed my initials stamped in gold. I scraped them off with a penknife, and then, without a backward thought, I packed.

I telephoned Andrew. When he heard that I was packed and ready to leave, he asked where my grandmother was. "Wait for me," he said, "I won't be long." And he rang off.

I would have to wait; he hadn't given me a chance to refuse. I went into the kitchen and ate biscuits and cheese. Grandmother was dining in San Diego and I had said I was going down to the Pepper Tree restaurant. I had forgotten about food until now when I had nothing to do but wait. Eating was positive and active; I was *not* going to stand about thinking *this is the last time*. When I had finished the cheese, I took a bowl of fruit out to the patio.

I was halfway through the fruit when the doorbell rang. Andrew stepped into the room, dwarfing it by his bulk in a thick greatcoat turned up at the collar. He took off his hat and his face was red from the wind. He looked perfectly calm, with something of the manner of a doctor when a familiar illness has entered the next, foreseen, stage.

"Of course you mustn't go off," he said, "but *now* I can put my oar in. I can talk to your grandmother." He looked round at the exquisite order, at the lack of ashtrays, and made for the patio door. In the garden he offered me a cigarette and we paced up and down. He would find a solution "within the framework of family and security"— anything else would be nonsense. I should unpack, go to bed, and forget about it all. Did I have something interesting to read?

"To the Lighthouse and *Mornings in Mexico."*

"Your taste or your grandmother's?"

"Shared. She bought them."

Presently Andrew said that we must give her her due. "She *is* an extraordinary woman. Her prejudices do not mean that she hasn't moved with the times."

I saw him into the car and off, and afterwards I did exactly as he had said. Instead of sitting about, as I had a tendency to do in an empty house, I got into bed. I was too tired to read more than a few pages. I turned out the lights and instantly fell asleep.

XIII

IF ANDREW TOLD my grandmother how close I had come to bolting, she never referred to it. The next day was the same as the day before, and the next and the next. The two must have met and talked together because Grandmother's manner had changed; she no longer prodded at me, but when the meeting had taken place and how long it lasted was not revealed. No slip of the tongue gave it away.

Some ten days later, after dinner when we had wandered out to the patio engrossed in a discussion of Virginia Woolf, my grandmother suddenly broke off. She had been fifteen, she said, when she and my grandfather had come to an understanding. Naturally they had not married until she left Vassar, but she had had that certainty from an early age. "The nature and instincts of a young woman cry out for a place in society, for a realm of her own, her own home. That comes late nowadays; the young do not marry early." Probably that was a reason they were so restless and dissipated—the denial of nature. Unable to assuage a natural craving, they turned to jazz and speed and drink— anything that battered the senses. She found it wicked, the most wicked waste of all. That was why she had been angry.

Anger led nowhere, and so she had set herself to the thinking out of a plan. Vassar was no answer to a young woman's instincts—and mine seemed fully developed. David Prentiss was no answer, either, for me. She could have told me that from the beginning, but she thought I should find out for myself. What then, until I fell in love? At the moment, living here with her was an aggravation.

Andrew had come to the rescue. He had suggested that I live with him in Laguna. She had thought it over, and it had seemed to her a splendid idea. It was more nearly what I needed—a life with a man. And I would be the mistress of a house. "Andrew," she said, "is a good linguist and he promises to keep you to your French. It will not hurt to try it out."

I put up no opposition, although I disagreed with everything my grandmother had said about a young woman's instincts. I did not cry out for, or crave, a home of my own or a life with a man. The very prospect of a long stretch of time alone with Andrew made me uneasy. That we got on well enough I put down to the effort we both made, and which could be made for an hour or two. And there had always been that double courtesy—his toward a woman, and mine toward an elder—which left me with the impression of the poor cat's paws on something hot: it demanded constant attention and agility.

I knew it was no use saying any of this. My grandmother had made up her mind, and I saw no alternative. I realized that she and I, for the time being at least, had come to a deadlock; any change would be for the better.

The transfer took place directly after lunch the next day with no further discussion or chance to waver. It went without a hitch: Andrew was there in the car, my cases were piled in, Grandmother stood at the top of the steps in the doorway and remarked that it was a splendid day for a drive. We were off with no more fuss than for a picnic.

Andrew's manner, too, was casual. Following a timeworn ritual, he decried Grandmother's habit on fine days of saying that the sea was as blue as, if not bluer than, the Mediterranean. Could not she see that the Pacific had its own color and romance? I was glad that Andrew did all the talking, but it was as though he thought his words, by ignoring what was taking place, would leave me less conscious of it. On the contrary, I was more aware. I would have been suspicious if there had been anything to suspect. I noticed that it was Grandmother who had set the tone by not saying goodbye.

Seal came out to meet us. He had gray on his muzzle and walked in a stiff sedate way. I was surprised that he recognized me after such a long absence. I had not been here since Augusta's death and I dreaded going into the house. Andrew had changed the look of everything. He had built a seven-foot wall at the back, which made a protected place to sit. Vines had grown and now formed an arbor outside the glassed-in dining room. Even the drawing room looked different: the grand piano was gone. Andrew's William Morris tapestries were on the walls, and a wide handsome table backed an unfamiliar divan in front of the fireplace. Augusta's room had been turned into a library; books filled the walls from floor to ceiling. The guest room was now cream-color and the very shape had been changed. It was smaller, with a private bathroom and deep built-in cupboards. I was flattered that Seal stayed with me; he lay on the floor pretending to sleep, while I unpacked.

The house was some miles from Laguna, quite isolated, sheltered by a number of ancient shaggy eucalyptus trees. The high wall at the back was against the main road. The front of the house faced the sea a short quarter of a mile away. My room was at the front and looked out through the big trees over a windbreak of young eucalyptus onto dunes which hid the beach but not the dazzle of the sea. With the window open, I could hear the breakers. That was as I liked it to be.

Andrew took me out to the new guest house. He had been keeping himself busy with building and rearranging everything. The guest house was two steps from the side door and was really a very large laboratory; there were two rather sketchy guest rooms and a bathroom, but it was the laboratory that interested Andrew. He showed me the working arrangements and then he took me over to his new microscope. He slipped one glass slide after another into position so that I could see how wonderfully it magnified his specimens. He was engaged in an entirely unexplored field of biological research and spent his mornings at it.

He thought I should have my mornings to do what I

liked: walking, bathing, reading. The afternoons and evenings we would spend together. We sketched out a very simple pattern of days; one differed from another only by whether it was the afternoon for my French or the afternoon to drive into Laguna for the mail and fresh vegetables. The postman did not come to the house; Andrew had a box at the post office. He didn't even want his mail every day. I think he liked to feel he was in a fortress with the drawbridge pulled up. Of course there was a telephone, but Andrew did not go near it.

One morning when I had been at the house for a week, I heard a bell and went first to the door. It rang again, and this time I knew it was the telephone.

It was Mrs. Randall, who said she had wormed it out of my grandmother where I had got to. Didn't I think it was unkind to disappear without letting my friends know?

I asked if Sonia was coming home this summer.

She was having such a gay time, Mrs. Randall said, that she was staying on indefinitely.

When I had said how happy I was for her, I could not think what more we had to talk about.

Mrs. Randall seemed to be having some difficulty herself. She rambled on about how much she admired my grandmother. My thoughts had begun to wander when I heard her say that it was up to us to protect her.

"Protect her from what?" I said.

I *dared* ask that, Mrs. Randall said, when I was responsible for placing my grandmother in the intolerable situation. Going off, living with a *man*.

"I am studying with my uncle."

"With your aunt's husband."

"French," I said.

"Think it over. And don't say I didn't warn you." The telephone had gone dead.

Augusta had bewailed the difficulty of keeping a servant in such an isolated house, and I had often wondered how Andrew managed on his own. Now I found that he was a tower of strength and resources. The house ran itself. Andrew went to bed late but this did not prevent him from being an early riser. Thus he had a number of hours more than anyone else. He made good use of time; whatever he did was planned, organized, shipshape. I do not know when the house was cleaned and dusted, but cleaned and dusted it always was—except for my room, which I looked after rather laboriously myself.

Andrew did not believe that a woman's place was in the kitchen. No woman, he said, had the slightest conception of cooking. She never measured or weighed anything. She was equally casual about timing. She was slow in her movements and slovenly in her habits. She knew nothing of the theory of food nor had she a palate.

Andrew was both vehement and lyrical on the subject of food. I was allowed to watch what he did, but only if I stood well out of the way.

Eating was, each time, a feast.

Fortunately for me, a woman had no idea of how to wash up, either; she put coffee filters into *soapy* water.

The mechanics of living took a surprisingly short time. The day was full of leisure, and I was offered the cream of it. What would amuse me? What did I want to do? The car was there to take me anywhere. I had but to say the word. The world was mine on the understanding that Andrew and I shared it. I saw that it was unthinkable that I get in touch with Thorn or Thistle and go out for an evening dancing. I was committed. I was committed, anchored to one person, tied; and yet my wishes were deferred to. When I thought it over, it seemed to me that I had now entered that other sphere: the adult world.

The entrance had been gentle, almost imperceptible, and I sometimes wondered if it weren't playacting, a dress rehearsal in borrowed finery. Finery there was, too, in plenty. After dinner one night, when I had begun to think I had lived there forever, Andrew brought out a box of jewels. I recognized rings and necklaces and brooches I had seen on Augusta. Andrew said there was no reason I should not make use of them as long as I was living there with him. Valuable jewelry and precious stones had very little meaning for me; it was more painful than pleasing to wear these reminders of Augusta, but—out of politeness—I did not see how I could refuse.

I do not remember quite how it happened, but another evening Andrew said I had very nearly Augusta's figure, and to prove the point he fetched a dress of hers for me to try on. It fitted like a glove. And then he said that Augusta had had the curious habit of keeping stored away, in their original boxes and tissue paper, a number of dresses which she had never put on. I might as well have these new ones. Dozens of pairs of shoes, too, quite unworn. He shook his head at the size of my feet; my aunt, he said, had a tidy foot.

When it grew warmer, I spent the mornings on the beach,

on the empty sand in front of the house. Andrew would have packed up a picnic lunch and would drive down to the shore. If he wanted to bathe, we'd eat our lunch there under a large canvas umbrella; otherwise, we'd explore inland or along the coast for a view and a tree for shade. On my French days I read a novel aloud to Andrew while he lay with his eyes closed after lunch and sometimes corrected my pronunciation. We kept on with the Wednesday matinee in San Diego; we looked forward to it and talked about it afterwards, and driving into town once a week solved the problem of heavy shopping. Toward the end of summer we even went as far afield as Riverside. Andrew still owned land and houses there and had to go at intervals to look after things.

On the way there we stopped at the Lion's Grove for a picnic lunch. The first time I had stopped here with Augusta and Andrew seemed to have happened in a forgotten age. What a child I had been! Andrew talked about that time; he had tried out a new proportion of gin to vermouth. He spoke of it as though it had been the day before yesterday.

In Riverside we stayed at the Inn, which was famous for its old-world décor and the cooking. It was then that it became plain to me that Andrew did not want to see other people. In Laguna, which was a new place, it was understandable that he spoke to no one, but in Riverside, where he had lived for many years and knew everyone, he kept himself just as aloof. He made no effort to see his friends. We had our solitary festive dinners together in the candlelight. If a man came up and spoke, Andrew was polite and short and did not suggest that he join us—not even Mr. Trevelyan whom I remembered as a very intimate friend.

Afterwards Andrew admitted that he might have been more cordial. It was Augusta who had loved people and parties and constant company. He had always preferred being alone with her. Now, he said, he was running his life more in his own way. He looked at me and asked if I minded. Talking to Mr. Trevelyan was not my idea of fun. But if we had been friendly, we would have been asked to his house; I would have met the twins and all the young ones and everything would have been quite different. It did not seem my place to say this to Uncle Andrew. I began to see that this was exactly what he did not want: that I should be swallowed up by a group of young ones. Andrew might like to be alone, but alone with a companion. I decided that this sort of life could be tolerated if it didn't go on too long. I was very conscious of its being holiday time, everyone was at home, parties and fun were going on everywhere, and I was missing it.

I could not very well ask Andrew how much longer I was supposed to be staying with him. Running away from Grandmother now seemed a childish whim in comparison to the need I foresaw for the future. I wondered if I shouldn't prepare myself for some sort of emergency job. I might learn to touch-type. Andrew had a typewriter at home which he had said I could use. Before we left Riverside, I went out and bought a typing manual.

Every morning I gave up an hour of the time I could have been on the beach to blind finger exercises. I stuck to it, in spite of the fact that it seemed as farfetched as the maiden in the tower plaiting her hair into a rope to escape by. Andrew appeared to see nothing unusual in my wanting to learn fast typing. He teased me about immobilizing his machine by pasting dark pads over the keyboard.

The days grew shorter, the wind from the sea chilly, and in the evenings we lit a fire, although this was more for cheerfulness than heat. And Seal so obviously loved lying stretched out in front of it. Dinner was earlier so that we could have long full evenings; Andrew had a stack of books he wanted to read aloud to me. He did not agree with me about the new experimental writing which went on and on about reality and the stream of consciousness. He was conscious enough of everyday life. What he wanted from a book was an escape into a romantic world. This stack of books was to be an attempt to convert me to his point of view. As a young man, he had been interested in the Pre-Raphaelite movement—and, as so often happens, he became fixed in that period in which he felt himself to have been a vigorous figure; he was somehow fastened there. For the same reason, the sea, the Far East and especially Japan, interested him. In a way, he looked at Japan through Pre-Raphaelite eyes; he saw it as innocent, decorative and noble. Among the books I noticed were a great many of Lafcadio Hearn's.

There were evenings when Andrew would even dress the part of escaping reality: he would appear after dinner in magnificent Oriental robes. My dress made a drab counterpart. Andrew would assure me that nature had meant the male to be resplendent; the female could be beige-gray without affronting any law. Modern dress had simply gone off the rails. Throughout the ages, it had been the masculine prerogative to be splendidly attired.

Andrew was fond of declaiming on masculine prerogatives; dress and appearance were a favorite opening—look at the lion, the peacock, look at the humblest of animal or bird. He spoke as a philosopher or teacher to a disciple, which gave me the uneasy sense that much more was to come. I was not a bit surprised on one of these resplendent occasions that Andrew took my arm and said, come, he was going to show me the foremost of masculine prerogatives. It is curious how many thoughts can go through one's head as one walks from one room into another. Andrew continued to speak in a gentle soothing voice, but I did not listen. I was think-ing of my grandmother and I felt certain that Andrew was not acting entirely on his own responsibility. I sensed that Grandmother was somehow back of him; perhaps she had asked him to smooth the way for me. She had always been too self-conscious or shy to discuss sex with me—and I quite understood how she felt; it would have embarrassed me, too. But in theory, at least, I knew that she was very matter-of-fact and broad-minded; I knew this by the way she had handed over to me her library of technical and theoretical books on the subject, including that monumental work of Krafft-Ebing. There was nothing, I felt, that I did not know. This was quite proved to be the case. It all went off like a dream that one is remembering: one knows what is going to happen because it has already happened in a sense. The only thing that astonished me was that a grown man should be reduced to near babbling.

Somewhere long ago I had read of a city of ancient Greece where it was the custom for girls, when they reached a certain age, to take part in a ceremony, the object of which was to lose their virginity to the statue of Apollo, because it was known that girls have a tendency to become irrationally infatuated by their first seducer. This custom was an astute precaution, or so the book said.

In the days that followed, I thought of this. I watched Andrew as he read aloud to me, as he quickly moved about the kitchen; I watched him across the dining-room table, and I knew I felt no differently toward him than I had before. I was, perhaps, more conscious of the gulf between our ages. Now he seemed elderly; I had never considered his age before. He, on the other hand, showed signs of a growing tenderness. He would hold my hand if I gave him a chance, he called me endearing names, he would leave his laboratory in the morning to look in at me. He'd stand behind me as I typed and suggest that we take a coffee together. He became curious, and even suspicious, of the letters I wrote or received.

One afternoon I jumped into the car and drove into Laguna to post a letter—the letter was unimportant and certainly not secret—I was simply feeling restless, and driving helped. I had often done this in the past and it had never been remarked; now Andrew questioned me. I said no more than that I had posted a letter, and Andrew sulked. He came out of it hours later when, under the cover of idle chatter, I said I had written to Mary Farnham, who was in a funk because she was taking her first job as a teacher in a girls' school.

And quite suddenly, with autumn settling down and everyone back at work, I began to get a whole string of letters, forwarded by my grandmother, from old Stanford friends. Dainty was going into films. What was I doing? Any chance of seeing me? Eddy Cavendish was still working on his symphony and for the moment he was supporting himself by playing the piano in a nightclub. Hal was a reporter on a Los Angeles paper. If I never came up, he'd drive down to see me.

Andrew wanted to know the reason for the flood. I said it seemed to be the time of year for letters, and gave him a few to read. They only made him fly into a temper. Couldn't those witless puppies mind their own business? He didn't want them here, hanging about the place.

Andrew's letting his temper run away with him like that made me cross. But I tried to speak in a reasonable way. I even said, "Let's be reasonable." And then, of course, I forgot to be, because it came over me that I was being held prisoner when in actual fact I was supposed to be about the business of getting married. And how on earth could my grandmother expect me to do anything about *that* if I never saw anybody?

Andrew subsided. He became quiet and persuasive. Young people nowadays rushed into marriage and out again for all the world as though they'd been caught up in a revolving door. They didn't know each other; they didn't even know what they wanted. I had always struck him, Andrew said, as sensible, and so he would put the matter to me sensibly. What were the highest expectations a woman could hope for from a marriage? He had seen enough of life to say straight off: an agreeable companion, a lively mind, a community of interests, an honorable man with sufficient worldly goods. Children, perhaps.

I could spend years rushing from party to party, from one dance to the next, without coming across a man who combined the attributes he had enumerated. Andrew leaned forward and took my hand. "I," he said, "can offer you all these things."

I felt at a complete loss. Never before had life appeared in such withered dimensions. I was not looking for cut-and-dried security. My wish from life was to live.

"Seventy and seventeen," Andrew said softly to himself. It was not strictly true, but he liked the phrase as he liked that of Beauty and the Beast. "We shall live happily ever after."

At his age, I could imagine that perhaps Andrew was tired. The life he was offering me was undoubtedly, to his mind, attractive. I thanked him and said that I could not possibly say yes. My answer did not perturb him. "Naturally," he said, "you must take time to think it over."

XIV

I_T IS TRADITIONAL_ that anyone, put under the shadow of thinking things out, be accorded a change of scene. Among the letters sent on by my grandmother was one from Jay Hamilton, inviting me to come to Pasadena for a while. I had already started a letter of refusal. Now I wondered. My time would be more or less my own in Pasadena. It was a chance to ransack the want ads in the Los Angeles papers and try to get a job.

The day before yesterday Andrew would not have let me go. Now, he quite saw that a few days away was a reasonable request.

The Hamiltons gave me a warm welcome and Camilla's

room. They were ideal hosts; they left me in peace. It was a great temptation to forget Andrew and sink into the pleasures of the moment. The Los Angeles newspapers were brought in with the breakfast tray. I ignored them on the first morning, but the fact that I had done so nagged at me all that day and even came between me and enjoying the dance at night.

I set to the next morning with a pencil and pad. Almost at once a notice struck me and I did not look any further. A capable young woman was wanted by the advertising office of Dobbs, *the* department store of Los Angeles. The more I thought about it, the more I liked the idea of advertising. It was something to put your mind into; it was a career women were making a name in, and there was the pot of gold at the end.

I buttonholed Jay as soon as he came into the drawing room. He looked skeptical. He said he knew that a great many young ladies had ideas of that sort nowadays. Even Camilla had wanted to do something or other, but of course he had discouraged her. Did I realize the long hours and the kind of people I would be in contact with?

I said I was a special case because of being thrown out of the university. I couldn't just stay at home and mope.

Jay saw that.

I could tell that he was wondering whether my grandmother would mind. I said she would be relieved to have me occupied.

"Hop to it, then," he said, and he telephoned to the garage for Hawkins. I tried to keep my mind from leaping ahead to the interview; I leaned back against the smooth silence of the movement, and when the Dobbs doorman ignored other cars and hurried over to the Rolls, I thought how his manner would change if he knew what I had come for.

As soon as I had gone through the swing door, I was as anonymous as a grain of sand; nevertheless the thought of Hawkins waiting for me in the street gave me a measure of Dutch courage. The advertising offices were difficult to find, hidden from the lushness and the gleam of the customers' tempting ground, behind a plain wooden door marked PRIVATE. Salesgirls, as indifferent as rock, had been misdirecting me to the complaint counter. Later I realized that they did not listen; they were interpreting my intentions. I should have come up by the staircase for employees.

The advertising manager was tall and dark-haired, with a small black mustache. The mustache put me off for a second; then I recognized the expression in his eyes. It was like Jay's—open, friendly, the speculative look of a man at ease with power. I was on familiar ground. He must have felt so, too; he may even have had daughters my age.

"Why aren't you at college?" he asked. I told him the truth, which made him sit up. He asked a lot of questions but as though he were an ally. At last, he wanted to know if I could touch-type and I said yes.

The advertisement, he said, was for a private secretary (his), and it wasn't necessary to know shorthand. The salary was good. But he had gathered from our conversation that I was more interested in the advertising side. I said that I was.

Did I know anything about advertising?

Absolutely nothing, I said.

My answer seemed to please him. He said he expected a

vacancy in the advertising department in a few weeks' time, but it would be on the lowest rung of the ladder. Did I mind that? The salary was low, too—lower than for a secretary—but it was a field wide open to advancement. If I started by being a secretary, I'd have to stick to it. Which job did I want?

I said I would wait for the advertising job, and he wrote down my name and address. He promised to let me know a week in advance.

Now that I had a way out, life in Laguna seemed quite different. I saw that Andrew was gentle and kind. Being aware that I was about to hurt him ennobled his very being, his every gesture and action. I was the viper at an innocent bosom—innocent and unsuspecting.

I wavered very much on the surface, but underneath I had just enough sense to realize that I had to go through with it. If I changed my mind now, everything would fall back as it had been, with no light ahead, into darkness; and Andrew turned back into the ogre.

Time stood still and flew. With the same breath I prayed for a quick end and for the respite to go on forever. I had to keep the turmoil locked in me; I went through the days like a zombie. I thought it strange that Andrew noticed nothing.

When the letter did come, I told Andrew at once. I had done it so often in imagination that it came out automatically. I was conscious of a stillness from Andrew. Presently he said he had thought I had had something new on my mind. He had not asked because he was afraid it would turn out like this. Now that it had come, we must put a good face on it. "Mind you," he said, "I think you are a little fool."

I accepted this in silence. "You are too inexperienced to be anything else." He smiled now and took my hand. I would come to reason—in time. He hoped I would. He wanted me to know that I could come back at any moment. "This is your home and I am waiting for you. Is that fair enough?"

He was being all too fair. I burst into tears and he went about comforting me. I cried harder because it should have been the other way round and I was so relieved. At last I felt spent. Andrew stood up. "We won't speak of it again tonight. We will go on with our real life; this other is just a little adventure of yours—an idea you have to get out of your system."

That was on Monday evening. I was supposed to start work on the next Monday.

On Tuesday morning Andrew tackled the subject of my job as though it were a plan we had concocted together. He said he would drive over and make it right with my grandmother. I believe he knew how much he was touching me by making things easy. And it was true; everything he did for me made me feel more contemptible.

At noon on Wednesday Andrew put me on the train in San Diego. I was to have lunch on the train while he was going to our steak restaurant, do the week's marketing, and go—as usual—to the matinee. He talked about it enough to make certain that I had taken it all in.

I could not hold myself to mourning Andrew. As fast as

steam could carry me, I was headed for the unknown. I did not know Los Angeles; I had never stayed there. I had gone on shopping expeditions with Camilla and Mrs. Hamilton, and I had danced at the Biltmore; that was as much as I knew. Andrew had thought it sensible of me to go a few days early to find a place to live. It might not be easy, he said. Andrew must have known the place pretty well, but he did not suggest the name of a small hotel as a starting point. I think he wanted me to feel the full inconvenience of being on my own. Grandmother, too, possibly. She had given Andrew a hundred dollars for me, which was more than she need have given, but it didn't allow me to stay at the Biltmore. Where would I tell the taxi to go? I worried about it for a while; then I simply stayed on the train all the way through to Pasadena. I telephoned the Hamiltons from the station, and they said yes of course and to come at once. Ely Culbertson and his wife were staying at the hotel and were giving the Hamiltons bridge instruction in the afternoons. In the evenings they played bridge with friends who were also under the Culbertsons. The hotel had become a hive of bridge. The Hamiltons did not have time for anything else, but on the first evening when I was unpacking, Jay came into Camilla's room to ask me how things were going. In spite of a rather abstracted eye, he said, "Bully," in a convincing way and handed me a banknote. It was like being a child again and getting a tip on the way to school. When he had gone, I looked at it. At first I thought it was fifty dollars. It was a five-hundred-dollar bill. I had never seen one before. Could Jay have made a mistake? He wasn't a man to do that. With this money in my pocket I was safe. I could look for a place to live, in peace. The relief broke the tension of the past weeks; suddenly I knew I was dead-beat. I would stay here and rest until Sunday afternoon. Then I would hire one of those drive-it-yourself roadsters for a week; it would make it easy to find a hotel and to look for an apartment.

On Sunday I got away later than I intended. The Hamiltons gave a lunch party and it was five before I was packed into the roadster. I started out on the road Hawkins always took and then somewhere I must have missed a turning. I had been driving long enough to have come out the other side of Los Angeles and still the neat suburban lawns stretched on either side. Daylight was going, electric lights were springing up when at last I saw high buildings. I drove slowly now and found what I wanted: large enough and not shabby, a straightforward businesslike hotel. CAR PARK AT BACK. Inside was what I had hoped for: no luxury lounges, an efficient reception clerk and alert bellhops. The price was reasonable. I booked in.

The dining room was brightly lit and filled with men I imagined to be traveling salesmen. Afterwards at the desk I asked to be called at seven-thirty. I needed more time than most people to wake up and settle myself into the day. Andrew knew this and relied on it to help bring me to my senses. On the hotel card I had picked up at the desk was a sketchy street map of Los Angeles with the hotel marked in red. It was on the outskirts, far from the center. I put the map in my bag to be able to find my way back.

Although it is a common belief that anything which is unpleasant or uncomfortable is reality, I have always found the opposite to be true. I entered now a very unreal phase of my life. It was as though I had been blown off onto

159

another planet. At nine o'clock every morning I clocked in at Dobbs—my card was punched with the time—and I clocked out at five. During the first weeks I was left with just enough strength to get myself back to the hotel and eat and go to bed. The first few days were the worst, and for the silly reason that I wasn't used to standing on my feet all day. I would have sworn that I was far stronger and healthier than those pale thin women in black satin dresses who worked at Dobbs. But they stood up to a full day unruffled.

At the beginning, my job could not have been more simple; a ten-year-old messenger boy could have done it. I had to take the proofs of the next day's full-page advertisement to the buyers of each department and get them to initial their own articles and space on the page. Then I had to go the same rounds with the layout for the day after.

Mr. Walsh, the advertising manager, explained to me how it all worked. Each department in the store was independent and had to pay its own way. The buyers were the heads of their departments and they paid for the floor space in the building, they paid for their stocks, they paid for newspaper space and a share of the advertising staff expenses.

The buyers were tough. They all (except the ones who were being featured) shouted that their space was at the bottom of the page, off in a corner; the drawings weren't detailed, the text not glamorous. Couldn't we put some pep into it? The buyers, who held their positions by showing substantial credit sheets, fought tooth and nail for a few vulgar superlatives. They scribbled them into the layout. Mr. Walsh fought back for good taste and restraint (it was the policy of Dobbs). He crossed out their scribbles. It was a daily battle. What it meant, to me, was that I was kept running back and forth.

By lunchtime on the first day I found that my stockings, from the ankles to the knees, were wringing wet with sweat. I walked up the block to a dark quiet coffee room near the Biltmore, where I used to meet Camilla. It was not crowded at lunchtime because it served Continental coffee, whipped cream, and Viennese pastry. I ordered one black coffee after another and chain-smoked through the lunch hour.

At five o'clock we workers streamed out of the side door. The traffic was already jamming and another lot would be released at five-thirty. I might as well take a chance now. When I reached my own room at the hotel, I lay down on the bed. To go downstairs to the dining room seemed beyond me. And why should I? I was my own master; I could do as I liked. Or rather, what I was able. I had a vague idea that I should put something inside me. I rang for room service.

A rather uppish youth answered and said that no meals were served in the rooms. I remembered something Dainty had told me. I handed him a five-dollar bill and asked if he could bring me a bottle of whisky. I lay down again on top of the bed. In ten minutes he was back and had slipped into the room before I had a chance to say "Come in." He unwrapped a brown-paper parcel and stood the whisky on the table. It was in a Johnnie Walker Black Label bottle. He made no effort to give me the change—that's what Dainty had said about hotel boys. I propped myself on one elbow and said, "Thank you." He started for the door and, almost there, he veered, and before I knew what was happening, he had flung himself at me. The thought went through my head: the hired car looks rich, and he's seen my wad of money. Where my spare strength came from, I don't know. I had pushed him off the bed, and while he was getting to his feet, I opened the door. He tried to pin my arms to my sides but I slipped out of his grasp and gave him a terrific shove. I went on shoving until he was outside. I bolted the door. Poor idiot! Now I would have to move as soon as I could.

I poured some whisky into a glass and sniffed it. It seemed all right, but of course you could never tell absolutely. It tasted right. I filled the glass with water and drank it. I thought about the bellhop. I was pleased to find that I didn't mind handling a man of my own age. It was only in the presence of my elders and betters that I was as weak as water.

Next door to the Viennese pastry shop was a small hotel. One scarcely noticed it: a doorway and a discreet sign. The rooms were smaller and darker than the suburban palace, but for the present I needed no more than a place to sleep. I booked a room for the following day.

The roadster stood unused in the car park near Dobbs. That it had been an extravagance rankled; but how could I have foreseen how tired I would be? I would look for an apartment on Sunday morning. I couldn't stay indefinitely at the hotel; the room cost more than my salary.

But when Sunday came, I stayed in bed until lunchtime. The big part of the afternoon went in driving the car to the Pasadena garage and in catching a train back to Los Angeles. I did not telephone or go to see the Hamiltons. In one week their world had become remote. That evening I wrote my overdue letter to Andrew. I had kept putting it off because I knew I must make it sound lighthearted. I made up jokes about being a messenger boy and about the people who went to the Viennese pastry shop. I admitted that I hadn't found an apartment yet. I did not mention how tired I got. I felt like the man transformed into a donkey who is blindfolded at dawn and attached to the long wooden arm at the well; all day long he walks round and round, lifting up the water, and at nightfall the bandages are taken off and he stands in his stable staring out into the darkness. It did not enter my head to escape to Andrew.

After the second week I was less tired in the evenings. I watched the newspapers for apartments or rooms. What I could afford was of a uniform ugliness. At last I took a one-room apartment a quarter of an hour by bus from Dobbs. I took it because there was a bright-looking kitchen with a refrigerator and a bathroom with a shower. The bed folded back into the wall, leaving two mustard-brown armchairs, a square table and a lamp. In practice, the kitchen-breakfast-nook was more cheerful for sitting and reading.

I held back from letting Hal or Dainty know that I was in Los Angeles. I still felt like that donkey. The rhythm of my days had nothing to do with my past. Also, I had been curiously chastened by the atmosphere of working in a department store. What did it was being herded through the employees' door with a time card which was punched morning, noon, and night. I felt the sense of difference between an employee and the meanest of customers, the free people, the public who could wander in and out at the door. *The customer is always right* is an insidious doctrine;

it seeped through from the trade counters to the advertising department. We were the slave peoples.

I did not make new friends at the store. In the evenings I went to the moving pictures by myself or I worked on Andrew's idea of mixing potassium permanganate with glycerine. I had rigged up a makeshift laboratory in the kitchen. I ground the permanganate crystals with a stone mortar and pestle which I had found in an antique shop. If I mixed the powder with glycerine too fast, it burst into flames. I wrote to Andrew that the inflammability made the mixture impractical. He answered that if I persisted in working in the kitchen, I should be careful not to knock sugar into it or I would find I had whipped up an explosive similar to TNT. He promised to send me some oil made from Japanese seaweed, the kind that was often used in cosmetics. It did not have the alarming potentialities of glycerine.

Within a few months, my office job had shifted completely. I was no longer a messenger boy. I had learned the various type faces and was shown how to mark the layout for the printers. For some time, I had been writing the descriptions of articles. From that, Mr. Walsh had moved me on to thinking up lead lines, the idea to hold the page together. He believed that each full-page advertisement should be like a poem or short-short story, hung onto one central idea. At that time it was an innovation in department store advertising. As Dobbs had a full page every day, it kept me on my toes, thinking.

Office work day after day, all day long, gives a different value to time. Months melted away. Warm weather was here without my having noticed the spring. My salary had been increased three times. Now I was respectably earning my living. In spite of getting pay envelopes every two weeks, I had never really got used to the fact. Each time, the envelope seemed out of the blue—unconnected.

I began to see why Mr. Walsh had forced me so rapidly. There was one woman in the office still above me; and now that I could handle all the newspaper work, she more and more often took days off. Mr. Walsh told me in confidence that she was going to have a baby and had given notice for July. Did I think I could manage by that time? I did not see why not. I had been doing her work for ages and I had three people under me. The top job was not as exhausting as the running about. The only drawback was that you couldn't leave by the clock but had to stay on until the proofs and layout were complete, ready, and collected.

I hadn't moved from my ugly one-room apartment; I hadn't had time. After the third increase in salary, I opened a charge account at Dobbs. It seemed reasonable to shop there; all employees were given a 10 per cent discount, and it was convenient. A charge account did away with the bother of cashing checks or carrying cash. I had to fill in a form and give two references. I gave Grandmother's and Andrew's names.

About a week later I was called to the office telephone, the first time that had ever happened. I thought it must be Hal. At the beginning of the week I had met him by accident in the street, and he had asked me to go with him on Saturday evening to a symphony concert at the Hollywood Bowl.

It was Andrew's voice. He said he was telephoning a

warning. My grandmother was on the warpath. She was angry about my opening a charge account. She was convinced I would run up a large bill, and she would be held responsible. He had not been able to calm her down. She was on her way now to Los Angeles to have it out with me. He did not think she would come to Dobbs but make a surprise visit to my apartment after work. Andrew wished me luck.

There was nothing I could do, or prepare, except myself. It was a bore that she was coming on the evening I had promised to go out with Hal. He was coming straight from work and he was not reachable during the day.

I left the office as soon as I could that evening, took a shower and dressed myself carefully. I dusted the living room and put fresh water in the flowers. The room was more pleasant in warm weather with the windows open. I realized I was doing everything to keep myself from thinking of my grandmother's anger. Now I faced it and it seemed absurd. I had acted within my own new freedom. I felt a twinge of sadness, but how different that was from guilt.

When the bell rang, I opened the door and there was Grandmother in front of me, smaller than I remembered. Perhaps I did not show the astonishment I should have, but I was moved by her fragility and the dearness of familiarity; I was genuinely pleased to see her. The warmth of my welcome took her by surprise. Before I had a chance to explain that a man was coming, Hal rang. I introduced them and told Grandmother that I was supposed to be going to a concert with Hal. Hal apparently liked Grandmother at once and asked if she wouldn't join us. Grandmother said that if it was the concert at the Hollywood Bowl, it was something she particularly wanted to hear. She invited us to have dinner with her first. She left the choice of restaurant to Hal, and it was fortunately very much to her taste, quiet with excellent food. The evening went off on sure feet. The concert was very good; Furtwängler was conducting, and the Hollywood Bowl made a superb setting on a warm night. During the interval Hal asked me about my job, and I was able to tell Grandmother about my raises in salary and the change in my position at the office.

We were still elated by the music when we got back to the apartment. Hal said goodbye in the street and drove off in his car. Grandmother kissed me affectionately and said how much she had enjoyed the evening and what a charming young man. She said it was goodbye for now, because she was driving back to La Playa early the next morning.

It wasn't until I had let myself into the apartment and saw those stiff chairs and table and lamp that it came back to me that I had been waiting for a scolding when I had come back from the office.

On Sunday evening Andrew telephoned again. There was real curiosity in his voice. What had I done to my grandmother? Her anger had been turned into the milk of human kindness; she had been bewitched.

I said that we had gone to a concert; she had not mentioned the charge account.

Andrew said that surely the gods had intervened. And I agreed; the evening had felt like that, under a special grace.

XV

Soon after I came to Los Angeles, I had answered a letter from my stepmother who had left journalism to be married again and was now living in Chicago. Old ties had worn thin but we kept up a token correspondence, a couple of letters spaced out in a year. My grandmother had never approved of her. So during the first months of office work, when I had felt somehow let down by and cut off from Grandmother, I had written a longer letter than usual to Ann, telling her about being on my own in Los Angeles.

Ann had always been most scrupulous in keeping up a certain reticence and distance. This time, she answered at once. She wrote that a friend of hers, Walter Dane, was coming to stay in Los Angeles on a long business trip, and that she had given him my address. I could depend on him. She added that he was handsome and an athlete like my father. As the months passed and Walter Dane did not materialize, I forgot about him.

On the Monday evening after my grandmother's visit, my doorbell rang. My first thought was that she had come back. A man was at the door. "You don't look like your mother," he said. And I knew who he must be. Walter Dane was not handsome nor did he have the appearance of an athlete. He was large and blond with a loose jovial face. He might be a salesman. He was something of the sort, connected with a big rubber company—Goodyear or Dunlop. His work in California had to do with the promotion of dirigibles. He was fixed up at an airfield the other side of Hollywood. He said all this before he had sat down.

The moment he sat, he said, "Let's scram and eat." On the way to the restaurant he told me that Ann had been a godsend to him in promoting dirigibles in the Middle West. "She is a fine newspaper woman," he said. "She's got gumption." Poor Ann, I thought; perhaps if gumption is suppressed in private life, it bobs up somewhere else.

We had man-sized steaks and a stack of French fried potatoes in a restaurant and district I didn't know. Walter Dane enjoyed talking; eating did not slow him down. I was told exactly how the wife and kiddies were installed in a house on the edge of the airfield. How he owed the big leg-up to Ann, and that anything he could do for her daughter he would consider a privilege. (If Ann had given the impression that I was her daughter, I felt I should not deny it.) He offered me the freedom of the airfield. He could have me flown anywhere I liked. He was staging a series of air races over the summer. I might enjoy watching them? In races, the takeoffs and landings were worth seeing.

An airfield offered a new world and a way out of the rut I had let myself fall into. Hot summer days were passing outside the open window with no more substance than scenery thrown onto a film screen. It was stupid not to get out of town on Sundays. I promised to come to the airfield. Walter Dane told me which bus to catch. He'd run me back in the evening; it was a privilege.

It *was* the freedom of the airfield. I found that Walter Dane was in charge. At the time of the Women's International Race, I sat in the control room and the gossip there was hair-raising. To the spectator it looked normal; planes sideslipped to a quick stop and were off again, but I heard that on the way across the continent competitors sabotaged each other's machines at night: sand in the engines, sugar in the gasoline. Surely if it were true, there wouldn't be a plane left in the race?

I went up in amazing old crates—like flying in streetcars. I think they were being tested to see if they could still do it. The men who took them up were capable of flying anything. In one, the engine cut off when we were high over Los Angeles, miles from home. We glided on air currents, as nice as you please, back to the familiar runway.

Walter Dane let me help him with some of the clerical work and reports on the races. Then he'd drive me back to town and we'd dine together. I had never set eyes on the wife and kiddies. I wondered what they did on Sunday evenings. The last time I was to see him—although I did not know this then—we were very late in getting away from the airfield. Walter Dane said would I mind if we stopped in Hollywood. There was a man he wanted to see on business, Pat O'Hara.

I suppose I expected an Irishman, perhaps in the dirigible business. Walter Dane rang the night bell to a very grand antique shop. It was dark and looked deserted. He lit a cigarette and said that it took a long time to get here from the inner sanctum. At last, a small door at the back opened, silhouetting a short squarish man. He did not turn the shop lights on. Probably he could see us in the gray half-light. "Come in. Come in," he said. "I got your message." We followed him toward the small door. This front room was wide and deep and filled with priceless objects, if one could tell from shape and gleam. The room that was lit was piled with Oriental carpets, some spread to show the color and design. I was dazzled by the light. "You like them?" said Pat O'Hara. "Feel the silkiness. Beautiful?" He belonged to that setting: as Oriental as the carpets. He wore a diamond ring and correspondent's shoes.

We went through another room of carpets and another and into—how right Walter Dane had been to call it the inner sanctum—a small room, satin-quilted or giving that effect. It was lit by a ceiling light with a green shade pulled low over a solid broad polished table. One chair was pulled up under the light and a powerful-looking magnifying glass lay in front of it. In a darker corner stood a tray with bottles and glasses. "We arrange the lady; then we talk," Pat O'Hara said. I refused the sweet liqueurs in favor of the vodka. "I, too, am Russian," said Pat O'Hara.

"Don't go," Walter Dane said as they went out to talk. I do not know how he expected me to go. I had had the impression that Pat O'Hara locked each door as we came through it. I ate cheese biscuits between fiery swallows. The room had seemed small because one side was filled by a four-poster bed, covered with dark red velvet. It had red velvet curtains. The other side of the room, I noticed now, was solid with steel strongboxes—the satin quilting was painted, *trompe l'oeil*. I went over to a side wall and touched it: it was real satin, pale gray. I poured out another vodka, and drank it slowly, while I examined objects through the magnifying glass: the cheese biscuits, the bottle labels, the material of my jacket.

Pat O'Hara was alone when he came back to the sanctum. He said that Walter Dane had had to go back to the field.

I looked at my watch and said that I must go, too. I didn't for a minute think I would ever get out of this core of the apple, but I couldn't imagine what the game was. If it was white slavery, pretty girls were a dime a dozen on any street corner. "Because I haven't eaten yet," I added, to give a reason for immediate action.

He poured out a glass of vodka and tossed it into the back of his throat. "I take you to dinner. Come." We wormed our way back through the rooms into the street. Escape was as simple as that.

We got into an extravagantly nickel-plated car which he said was an Isotta Fraschini. Didn't I like his car? and did I like Russian food? because Sunday was club night. We parked behind a line of cars in front of a private house and went through a gate into grounds that looked dilapidated because of the pepper trees, and through the open door into an antechamber where a hatcheck girl sat.

Pat O'Hara said something in a language I didn't understand, and we went on into a room full of tables and people.

A waiter seated us directly in front of what appeared to be a stage. The curtains were down. Pat O'Hara ordered as the menu was in Russian. We had cold borsch with an island of sour cream, blinis with caviar. The food was exquisite, in contrast to the room and furnishings. There were no carpets and the tables were of cheap unvarnished wood. The air was thick with friendliness shouted in an incomprehensible tongue. I judged the tables to be made up of families, husbands and wives, because of the mongrel dog which lay under almost every one.

Pat O'Hara said it was a theatrical club, an intimate theatrical club. He came because of the chef and the plays. Russian and Yiddish companies came here. Here and New York. Tonight there were a couple of one-act mimes, but *The Dybbuk* was coming soon—the original company—and he'd bring me to that.

While we were eating I had a good look at my host. He was quite the ugliest creature I had ever seen. He embodied everything I had been warned against. One could not blame him for the sinister face, but he need not have committed himself to the wrong everything: clothes, diamonds, car. How on earth had he got an Irish name? It must have been clapped on, on top of everything, like the nickel plating on the Isotta Fraschini. He was redeemed by two things: scrupulous cleanliness and his manner, which was warm and kindly.

When the coffee came, Pat O'Hara lit a cigar. He said he owed me an explanation and an apology from Walter Dane. Walter had been too hurried—or too shy—to speak for himself. He had had to turn me over to him, he said, because his wife was kicking up a fuss. She refused to believe that I was the daughter of an old friend; she had seen me.

I didn't need to be *turned over* to anybody, I said. I was all right by myself.

Pat O'Hara shook his head. He said that a young woman needed a man to look after her.

"That is the very danger a young woman tries to avoid," I said, "being looked after by a man."

He laughed. "I'll put it on another basis," he said. "It interests me. And I'll tell you why it does. Because you look like a lady. I like to go to good restaurants and I like to puzzle my friends. If I am seen with a young college lady, the world is puzzled. With an older lady, it would be different. She might want a Turkey carpet or a Louis XVI table. But with you—you don't look as though you were after furnishings. . . ."

It would puzzle my friends too, I thought, if they were here to see me. Very well, dining out as a practical joke seemed harmless enough.

Los Angeles and Hollywood—if you include Beverly Hills, Santa Monica, and other outposts—have quite a number of good restaurants. We dined out about three times a week and covered a good deal of ground. On Sunday nights we went back to the Russian Theatrical Club where we both preferred the food, but, as Pat O'Hara said, it was not a place where his joke came off. "These people," he said, "are surprised at nothing, they are White Russians."

One night when he had stopped the car in front of my apartment, he asked if he could come up for a drink. I said of course he could, but I was rather tired and had to get up early in the morning. That was all he wanted to know, he said: whether or not it was possible for a man to come up. Did I mean that there were no restrictions?

I said it was like any apartment.

"It won't do," he said, and he scowled at me. "You could let yourself in for anything. Anyone could get you."

I said that the door was solid and that it locked.

"You might come home when you had already had something to drink."

"That's usual."

"Don't you see that you're too damned polite to live like that? How long a notice do you have to give?"

"A week."

"Hand it in tomorrow."

He telephoned the next evening, wanting to know if I had given notice. I said no, I hadn't. The apartment was near my work, and in any case, I wouldn't dream of rooming with a family, if that was what he had in mind.

It seemed that he had already fixed me up for the beginning of the next week at the Hollywood Studio Club for Girls. He said that it was a beautiful place, supported by the film industry for extras who didn't make much money; it was dirt cheap. He would be outside Dobbs the next day to drive me there.

The Hollywood Studio Club for Girls was a spacious building, modern Spanish, set back among trees, and inside it was a cross between a luxury hotel and a boarding school. Pat O'Hara showed off the patio and lounges as though he had built the place. We sat down on a divan. Very pretty girls kept walking through, and in the lounge young men were obviously waiting.

Men weren't allowed upstairs, Pat O'Hara said. It would only cost me—and he named half what I paid for my apartment—and that included breakfast, lunch and dinner.

I began to be interested. I had grown tired of the ugliness of my apartment. When I asked how I could get in, as I wasn't an extra, he said it had been arranged. His real business was films; the shop was on the side.

Pat O'Hara came in his car on Sunday afternoon to move me to the Studio Club. Two blocks from the clubhouse, at the corner of Vine Street, he slowed down and showed me where to catch the bus into Los Angeles. He insisted upon paying the extra week's rent for the apartment because he said it was his fault I hadn't given notice; he hadn't explained. "Now everything's shipshape," he said.

I saw exactly what he meant late that night when I lay propped up on pillows in the red velvet four-poster bed. Pat O'Hara had got up and had gone into another room to make tea. It was a pale green China tea and I was enjoying it. He was sitting on the side of the bed in a dark heavy silk dressing gown. There was nothing "wrong" about Pat O'Hara in a silk robe. "You see," he said, "I like being certain of my women. I like to feel they can't get into incidental trouble."

I did see, exactly.

Upstairs at the Studio Club, life on the practical side was very much like boarding school: the corridors, bedroom doors standing open, groups of girls. I shared a simple whitewashed room with a blond girl. She wasn't pretty but she was well made, which was not hidden; when I first met her she had only a pair of knickers on. "Hullo," she said, "I'm a pony. What are you?"

Pat told me afterwards that a pony was a chorus girl. I said I was in advertising. Pat had said that it was best to tell the truth. Nobody was going to put me out, once I was in.

At the Studio Club, I saw the raw side of film life. Many of the girls who lived at the club had a resemblance to some star and did the danger work for her: breakneck escapades on horseback; jumping or falling over cliffs, off ships, off skyscrapers; being knocked down, being run over. Calamity Janes, they were called, and they considered themselves lucky to come back to the club at night with a splint or a bandage, and not to be laid up in the hospital. The Calamity Janes were the rowdy ones at dinner. At the opposite pole, that of absolute stillness, was a girl whose face bothered me; I felt I must have met her somewhere before. She was an apparition of loveliness, and, like an apparition, she never said a word. She had the astonishing habit of pouring a small pitcher of ordinary cream over her ice cream before eating it.

I had made one friend at the club, a girl who waited for the same bus into Los Angeles in the mornings. She was in advertising, too, a commercial artist at Bullock's. She had been living at the club for years and knew everything. She told me that the apparition was Greta Garbo's double. She was Hungarian and perhaps she did not speak much English. She was in a state of permanent melancholy because she had come to Hollywood to be an actress in her own right. Of course there was nothing to be done with her; she was so like Greta Garbo that even the director couldn't tell them apart until he looked down at their legs.

Varya Nicholls—that was the commercial artist's name—gave me a good many useful tips. She took me to a swimming pool nearby where Club girls were admitted free. And on Sunday morning early, she drove me to some stables where we were given horses for practically nothing. Greta Garbo's double, Varya, and I were the only studio girls who went there early. Once, when we were standing together waiting for the horses to be saddled, I thought the double was going to speak, but she only smiled. (Several years later I ran into her in the powder room of the Ritz in Boston and she came up to me as though we were old friends. She talked a blue streak; she told her entire history from Hollywood to Boston. Thank heavens, she had gone on the legitimate stage.)

Varya Nicholls also tipped me off about putting my name down for a single room. One was free every so often, and it didn't cost any more. I did, and got one quite soon. As the ultimate seal of friendship, Varya shared with me her new *New Yorkers*.

Work at Dobbs was a matter of routine now, and I was training the girl under me to do all the jobs I did. Mr. Walsh rather jokingly said that when I had done that, I would be able to stay home with a cold.

Contrary to what the facts should have dictated, the change in my relationship with Pat O'Hara was a shortcut to trust. We each shared more of our own concerns. I learned that he had been unhappy and upset for almost a year. His wife had left him to marry a popular film star. I remembered the wedding from the newspapers. I said that the bride's name had not been O'Hara.

"She uses her film name," Pat said. After quite a long silence he went on, and it seemed to come out against the grain, he said that Pat O'Hara had been the name on his shop when he bought it. He had kept it for the business; everyone knew that it wasn't his real name.

I did not ask what it was.

"What's in a name?" he said.

I told him about my suntan lotion, which I had finally managed to mix smoothly with the seaweed oil. I explained the difficulties: as I didn't have the capital to put it on the market myself, the only thing to do was to sell the formula to some cosmetics firm. The trouble was that any chemist who looked at my product would know at a glance what the active ingredient was. It would have to be an honest firm.

"No firm is that honest," Pat said. He made an appointment and went with me to a new cosmetic firm which has since become world-famous. Pat said he could tell a trustworthy man a mile off. We were shown through the laboratories and factory by the manager. When we came out, Pat said, "You can't trust him; he's a Jew."

I showed my astonishment that he, of all people, should put it like that.

"Pot calling the kettle black," Pat said with a slight

question mark. "Jews *are* more honest than most men, but the other side of it is, they are that much more ambitious."

We decided to wait and try somewhere else.

Pat never burdened me with impassioned love talk; it even occurred to me that in making me his mistress, he considered himself to be conferring a courtesy due to a woman. Moving me to the Studio Club had been a matter of fastidiousness. He was a superlatively competent lover and needed no verbal reassurances. In any case, the question of love had never arisen. The sense of personal freedom which this left me with suited me down to the ground.

He continued to value my young college-lady look. He encouraged me to dress as though I had come off the golf course rather than properly for dining. It heightened the discrepancies between us; he thought it underlined the joke.

One night dinner had been particularly successful because a whole table of film people who knew Pat actually gave way to curiosity and surprise: they kept staring, and on their way out they stopped and spoke and obviously hung on for a clue or an introduction. That night, when they had gone away unsatisfied, Pat leaned across the table, his eyes shining, and said, "Damn it all, I don't see how you do it! Even now you still look as innocent as a glass of water."

A joke is a joke, but if it is carried on too long, nothing could be duller. And Pat's conversation was limited. I preferred the evenings with Varya. She talked about Gertrude Stein and Hemingway, D. H. Lawrence and Aldous Huxley, cubism, Gershwin's music. A new spirit, a new creativeness, was there for us; we both felt the excitement. Varya was trying to transmute *a rose is a rose is a rose* into commercial art. And she was doing pretty well at it. She was as good a commercial artist as anyone on the West Coast, and now she wanted to get into the real arena. She planned to go to New York. In the meantime, to keep herself from becoming set, she went to a life class three nights a week. Sometimes I went with her; I didn't want to be left out of anything.

It was a time when Pat O'Hara had his hands full with moving-picture business. Talking movies had started a revolution in Hollywood. Half the actors couldn't speak English, and another quarter couldn't speak understandably. Actors demonstrated in the streets; actresses were in tantrums. Popular demand sided for sound. Elocution teachers began to flock to Hollywood. Pat was kept so busy that the best he could do was to meet me on Sunday evenings at the Russian Club.

Perhaps if I had not been turned over to Pat O'Hara, I might not have been so quickly fed up with Los Angeles. With Pat, I had seen it all; I was familiar with every used-car park, gas station, restaurant, street corner. Los Angeles was an uninspired, sprawling, provincial conglomeration. Varya did not mince words about the place. It was a backwater. "Read *The New Yorker*," she said, "and you'll see."

In her drawings Varya had more scope for incorporating the new spirit—Gertrude Stein and Hemingway, D. H. Lawrence and Virginia Woolf—than I had with the prose of a department store. I was held in the cross fire between

Mr. Walsh and the buyers. The top had turned out to be as much of a groove as the messenger boy.

When Varya suggested that I come to New York with her in November, I saw that Los Angeles was dust and ashes. My only chance was to leave now, at once, before I had got used to a good salary.

Money was piling up in my bank. In July when I was put in charge of the office, my salary at Dobbs had been doubled. It was almost more than flesh and blood could bear to leave it.

Varya Nicholls very reasonably said, what if I did stay on at Dobbs all my life? Most likely I wouldn't even save money; I would spend it out of boredom. I would be old, and I would never have seen or done anything.

Yes, I would have to go.

XVI

"It is for you to choose. It is for you to decide" had been said—and resaid—by my grandmother since my first day in California.

I turned the gooseneck reading lamp away from my book toward the whitewashed wall. It was late, and I was lying in bed at the Studio Club, and I always turned the light like that when I wanted to think.

It seemed to me that I had never made a decision before. It was true that at times my grandmother had offered me two or more alternatives, but it had been like saying would I take the Ace, King, or Knave? And I had invariably said the Ace, please. There is not much decision in that. When I had left Andrew for a job, that was escape.

Was I even making a decision now? Did one ever? It wasn't the rights or wrongs which made me want to go to New York. It was instinctive: a necessity, a craving. What made my going to New York look like a decision was that, for the first time, I would have to sacrifice something—salary and security—to do what I felt impelled to do. Truthfully, to myself, I admitted that all the security in the world did not count for a hill of beans. My worries were Grandmother, Andrew, and Mr. Walsh—in that order. It was the irony of my fate that anyone who recoiled as much as I did from disappointing people (and the contingent unpleasantness) should be forced to do so at every step.

I snapped off the light and pulled the bed covers high over my head.

I woke up feeling happy and light. There was nothing to prevent me from writing letters to Grandmother and Andrew. I could say everything I needed to say in a letter, and probably more clearly. A visit to La Playa was out of my way, was a detour, a dead end. I would have to come back here to get the train to New York. If I went straight, I could be gone before unkind things were said, or feelings hurt; before I was prevented from going. I would write the facts, and they would speak for themselves.

After lunch, I went on to the Viennese coffee shop for some of their black dynamite. During the morning I had grown doubtful of the easy way out. Facts might speak for themselves, but would they speak for me? No. Letters would not do. I would have to go, and go through with it. Grasp the nettle. Take the bull by the horns. If I did not

184

go to Grandmother, I would have no peace of mind; I would be left with a vacuum at my back.

That afternoon after work Mr. Walsh brought up the subject himself; at least he opened the way to it. He said I had not yet had my vacation. I ought to think about it. He hadn't proposed it before because they couldn't have got on without me. But now that I had shown Miss Whitely all the tricks, they wouldn't even notice that I had gone.

"Do you really mean that?"

"Quite," he said. "Quite."

Then my intentions rushed out into the open.

Mr. Walsh looked incredulous. He asked if I were going to get married. Hiring women was the very devil; you wasted time and money training them, and as soon as your back was turned, they left you. Dobbs, he said, had treated me more generously than was usual anywhere.

I said it had nothing to do with Dobbs. I was quite aware that they had been generous and I appreciated it. It was Los Angeles. I found I couldn't stick it. I simply couldn't go on living there all my life.

It was a fine city, Mr. Walsh said, and I wouldn't find a better climate on God's earth. "Give us five years and we'll be the biggest metropolis in the West."

I said that seven out of ten of the inhabitants were Midwesterners who had come out to end their days. It gave a deadness to the atmosphere. I had not seen this so clearly until I had said it. There was a lot of truth in it.

"You've been working too hard," Mr. Walsh said. He proposed that I take the two weeks due to me before I made up my mind. And when he saw that that was no use, he shifted ground. He had hoped that we would have been able to cooperate for some long time. But if not, not. Technically they owed me two weeks' holiday with pay; I owed them two weeks' notice. One canceled the other out. I could leave at any time, but he would appreciate it if I could give Miss Whitely a couple of weeks with the knowledge that she would have to take over.

And so that was settled.

Pat O'Hara said I wouldn't like Broadway. It was tough and it was old-fashioned. "They're all dying to get out here where the money's big." Then it occurred to him that I wasn't interested in show business. "It's no place for a lady, I'll tell you." He wanted to know what I was going to do when I got there. "If you don't know, why in the devil are you going?"

I didn't mind what Pat said. But his questions were good as a dress rehearsal. Why? Why indeed? To get to the fountainhead, to be among people where thoughts were thought, to be in the place where events were shaped. It sounded vague and highfalutin. And I certainly did not say it aloud.

"I suppose you want to see the world?" he said.

It was as good an answer as any.

We agreed to make a clean break before I went to La Playa. On the last evening together we went to the Russian Club and sat in a corner away from the stage because Pat said we had to talk. We didn't talk a great deal. From time to time Pat gave me advice which might have been lifted straight from Anita Loos. He had friends on Broadway but he dismissed each in turn. "This will look after you," and he took a strong small brown envelope from his pocket. It was bumpy. He pushed it toward me with an embarrassed expression—a look I had never seen on his face. "Aren't you going to open it?"

As I reached for it, the spell was broken: he was all eagerness. Inside were four unset stones, half-moons in shape. He said that they were star sapphires.

"But I can't," I said.

He demanded why not. They weren't any use to him. He had got them for cuff links, but they were too fancy for a man. He lifted a shoulder and stretched out an arm to show his cuff. "You know where you are with diamonds."

I couldn't find it in my heart to give my opinion on that; I repeated that I couldn't take the sapphires.

"Look at it this way," he said, "it's not like cash that you blow when you are out of sorts. It's like an insurance policy."

"If only they weren't valuable," I said.

Pat began to look vexed. "That's the whole point. You'd make anyone think you were soft in the head, plumb crazy. Unless"—and a look of comprehension came into his eyes —"unless you think they're hot."

I had to laugh. Pat laughed, too. The waiter brought coffee; the lights were dimmed and the play began.

We left after the first act, and when I picked up my cigarettes, I noticed that the envelope had gone.

Months later in New York when I opened the back zippered compartment of the bag I had carried that night —it was a flat red crocodile one which I hardly ever used, and almost never the back compartment—I found the envelope. I put it in the bottom of my jewel case, where it stayed for a good many years: the insurance policy of Pat O'Hara, the name not of a man but of a shop.

During the two weeks of grace at Dobbs, I debated with myself: would it be better to warn Grandmother that I was going to New York or better to spring it when I was there? A letter might start a softening; equally, it would give her the chance to stiffen, as cement does with time. To reassure myself I said that it was my own affair, I was using my own money, I was asking for nothing but understanding. That was the rub: seen from the outside, was it understandable?

When I wrote to ask if I might come to La Playa, I did in the end say that I was going to New York. And then of course I had to write to Andrew; far better that he should hear the news from me. I had pictured myself trying to bring up the subject casually, and decided that it was wiser to arrive in the middle of an uproar. All I would have to do was to remain matter-of-fact as though it were natural. On the face of it, it was natural enough; Grandmother went East almost every other year, Sonia was still there, Camilla came and went—to her it was nothing. But would Grandmother see it for what it was—the final break, the severing of my dependence and her responsibility?

Grandmother did not come into San Diego to meet me; she sent the car. I knew, but I had to assure myself, that this meant nothing. She had never liked trains and stations. Dread might as well have blackened the sun; I noticed little from the car window.

I became conscious of a flood of sunlight and the more than realness of objects the moment I stood before Grandmother. I had walked through the drawing room and out to the patio where Grandmother was resting on the chaise longue. As I leaned down to kiss her cheek, she said, "How golden the autumn days are, here in the West." It was a remark she often made at this time of year. She asked me to move a chair so that she could look at me, and to take off my hat. I did not look as though I had had enough out-of-doors exercise. She supposed I had not been eating the right kind of food, either. What, she wondered, had induced me to move to Hollywood? Was I also infatuated with the moving-picture world?

I told her about the cheapness of living at the club.

Apropos of nothing, Grandmother said, "So you don't really like La Playa, after all?" She had always thought that I loved the sea and bathing, and yet I hadn't come home once during the summer.

I said that I hadn't had a vacation because I couldn't be spared from the office.

"And now you are leaving them completely?"

I started to explain the situation, but Grandmother lifted a hand. We would talk about all that after dinner. Andrew was driving over and we would have dinner at the hotel first. She told me about the summer: Edward Fowler was turning out to be a pleasant well-mannered young man; Mrs. Alden's two boys—what odd names they called themselves—Thorn and Thistle had asked for news of me. Sonia had been home for three weeks in July. Grandmother had seen her several times and she had not once mentioned me.

I said that I had not had a letter from her since my engagement to David Prentiss.

She gave me a cool look. Didn't I see now that I was apt to rush into situations without considering the consequences?

When I had finished dressing, Grandmother had not yet left her room. I stared out of my window at Soledad, that bare sun-scorched mountain which had been a part of my past. I remembered how in the beginning Soledad had meant the peace and liberation of solitude. Presently the sky above it turned pink. I went to the drawing room balcony to look out at the setting sun. It was sinking, round and red, into that vast stretch of water; it was almost over the brink. Why had I imagined this wide horizon a promise? I had not taken into account that it was where the sun set.

While I was standing on the balcony, the Delage stopped in front of the house. Andrew waved; he must have thought I was watching for him. He came toward me smiling, and I greeted him from the balcony before I went to open the door.

Dinner passed quickly in talk: amiable, on-the-surface topics; Andrew put himself out to hold our attention. I am positive he even invented incidents to make Grandmother laugh. His manner made me feel that he was going to prove an ally.

I was almost confident when we arranged ourselves in the patio for the talk. My grandmother was a voice, an indistinct figure on the chaise longue. Propped against it, her slender ebony stick reflected a point of light which came through the open French windows. The air was soft and dark and scented with jasmine. Andrew was completely in shadow; I merely sensed that he was there.

Grandmother had been speaking for some time, all very much what she had said to me after I had been expelled from the university: about being self-indulgent, thoughtless, and selfish. My going off to a job in the first place was a combination of all these things. There was no reason for me to work in an office; she was prepared to give me an allowance, large enough for me to be perfectly comfortable. Now she was old and infirm and in need of a companion. She hesitated at this point, and Andrew took up the spoken word.

I could not believe that I was hearing right. He was as harsh as Grandmother, *and* on similar lines: how he had taken me into his home and heart, had cherished and fêted me, and when any man who had done as much had a perfect right to expect gratitude, what had happened?

Grandmother joined in, and Andrew went her one better. I listened, horrified. I had not heard Andrew move, but I was aware of a hand on my shoulder, a brief pressure that was gone. It was about this time that Grandmother's and Andrew's duet had ceased to sound menacing and became a poker farce of outbidding each other. I understood now what Andrew was doing, and I saw that he had to keep it up. It was Grandmother who had to break down.

She did. In an extraordinary, good-natured chuckle. "We sound like a pair of ravens," she said. "How far we have strayed from the truth."

Grandmother must have shifted her position; the creak of the wickerwork betrayed the movement. I imagined that she had turned to face me. She spoke in a slow calm voice.

She remembered, she said, telling me on my first night in California that she was too old to adjust her ways to youth. That had been truer than she had believed in her heart. And then she made another statement, one that she had also made before: "Experience cannot be passed on to others. Each human being has to find out for himself."